Waterm

Writing by lido lovers
and wild swimmers

Edited by Tanya Shadrick & Rachel Playforth

The Frogmore Press &
Pells Pool Community Association, Lewes

First published in Great Britain in 2017

The Frogmore Press
21 Mildmay Road
Lewes
East Sussex
BN7 1PJ
www.frogmorepress.co.uk

In association with Pells Pool Community Association
www.pellspool.org.uk

Printed and bound by Clays Ltd, St Ives plc

A catalogue record for this book is available from the British Library.

ISBN 978 0 9570688 7 2

In memory of Lynne Roper
a wild woman swimming

Pells Pool

The Pells Pool, Lewes, is the oldest freshwater outdoor pool in the UK and has opened every year since its first season in 1861. Built to Imperial dimensions of 50 yards by 25 yards, the Pells was originally funded by subscriptions from the people and businesses of Lewes, and – having been saved from the threat of closure in the 1990s – it is now run by a community association and supported by the Town Council. Set alongside the Pells wetlands and drawing its water from springs beneath the Town Brooks, the pool is an important part of daily life for many Lewesians in its May to September season. It also brings in visitors to Lewes from across the region.

As part of its continuing work of local community engagement, the Pells appointed Tanya Shadrick as its first writer-in-residence in 2016.

Introduction

The connection between water and writing is an enduring one. In our most mindfully creative states we achieve flow, the rhythm and peace of swimming with our inner tide. Our everyday language is full of swimming metaphors and our relationship with water is also a relationship with existence and creativity. Both swimming and writing can be bracingly solitary or warmly communal; both hold the promise of comfort or danger.

In choosing the pieces for this anthology we were looking for writing that made those familiar metaphors strange again, showing us new waters and unique experiences. As F Scott Fitzgerald wrote, 'All good writing is swimming under water and holding your breath', and the writer-swimmers collected in this book take that underwater journey in fiction, truth and poetry – facing dark depths or finding a rhythm, embracing risk or coming home.

Lake Ontario. Skarðsvík. Isola Santa. Galway. Trollhagen. In waters from around the world, these writers immerse us in birth and death, danger and rescue, new loves and last. Ness Cove. Spitchwick. Thurlestone. Sharrah. Swimmers closer to home take us to places few know and less dare: freezing mountain pools; rivers in full spate where buoyancy is lost suddenly in froth and bubbles.

But even in the wildest swims and noisiest lidos, our writers keep watch for still, small moments of heart and mind. A child-philosopher measures joy not in money but time spent in water; after a lifetime abroad, an old man returns to home water like a salmon moving upstream; an adult daughter treasures the sight of her elderly mother plunging in, self-forgetful after years on the side.

Of all the fine work in the anthology, the poem that perhaps speaks for the whole is Anna Selby's 'Night Swimmers', in which almost every line begins with affirmation:

Yes it stained them
slapped them awake
Yes the water sang with them in it
Yes the echoes of their strokes at the edges
Yes they climb out altered

More than fifty writers of prose and poetry beckon us now into a book which is also a 'Yes', resounding and collective. To adventure, risk, depth, reflection. To encounters – solitary and communal – with the wild and free. To swims that have us climb out altered. *Yes*.

TANYA SHADRICK & RACHEL PLAYFORTH
Editors

Contents

Sea

1   *Thurlestone Rock* Lynne Roper

5   *The Decision* Malinda Green

8   *Triolet on the Sea Shore* Rosamund Taylor

9   *Shore* Jeremy Page

10   *Ness Cove* Emma Pusill

13   *Agnes & the Finman* Anna Kisby

14   *Swimming at Trollhagen* Mary Lowerson

15   *Sjórinn Freistar* Emma Beynon

16   *Skarðsvík, West Iceland* Tom Hall

19   *Selma and Ture* Jane Greene Pettersson

22   *Galway Blues* Tim Martindale

25   *Sundays at Rachel Finlayson* Rebecca Rouillard

28   *Two-thirds of Our World is Ocean* Redfern Barton

32   Patrick Taggart

River

37 *Spitchwick* Lynne Roper

39 *River Swimming* Wayne Tenyson

41 *Cloud Chamber* Janet Sutherland

42 *Buoyed By The Tides* Louisa Thomsen Brits

45 *A Swim Down River* Mat Christian Thomas

48 *The Ripple* Seema Kapila

51 *eeeooo* Mark Bridge

53 *The First Thing, Always, is the Cold* Hannah Linden

54 *Locomotion* Tara Gould

57 *Las Marejadillas* Maria Jastrzębska

59 *Mirror Image* Sue Robbins

60 *Unswimming* Holly Dawson

66 *Down the River* Alexandra Heminsley

Lake, Pool & Pond

73 *Sharrah* Lynne Roper
77 *Skye, Diving* Kaddy Benyon
79 *In Deep* Charlotte Ansell
81 *The Mountain's Voice* Jenny Arran
82 *Water Spirit* Clare Best
84 *The Non-Swimmer* Jill Munro
85 *In a Blue Lake* Graham Burchell
86 *Skinny Dipping at Isola Santa* Kathleen Jones
87 *Lake Ontario* Lindsay Zier-Vogel
89 *Rescue* Sarah Wallis
90 *Aquae Sulis* Zel Norwood
92 *Pond Hang* Clare Whistler
93 *Night Swimmers* Anna Selby

Lido

97   *They Can't Really Fly* Ed Broom
100   *Gene Pool Party Dude* Mark Fiddes
102   *Wake* Claire Collison
103   *The Lido Coat* Ia Jennings
104   *Moon* Annie Peel
106   *June '16* Louisa Wright
107   *July, Oxford* Jack Pritchard
108   *Dive Deep* Rachel Playforth
110   *Pickled Sunshine* Michelle Porter
113   *The Swancote* Lyn Thomas
115   *Pool Closed Today* Martin Gayford

117   Contributors

Sea

Thurlestone Rock
LYNNE ROPER

Thurlestone Rock, icon of the South Devon coast, sits around five hundred metres off shore at high tide, sturdy legs astride, and just begs to be swum through. It's near the end of a reef that runs perpendicular to the shore; the reef is legendary for its beautiful underwater garden of seaweeds and aquatic creatures. I'd not swum here before, and the 40 knot south-easterly whipping up the sea promised to make the swim slightly more sporting than we had expected it to be.

As we walked down the short track to the beach, my swim buddy JJ told us that on arrival he'd been immediately accosted by a local, who exclaimed at the perilous state of the sea and informed him that anyone attempting to swim would certainly be drowned and dashed onto the rocks. This was clearly an exaggeration, although we did have a chat before getting in about the best route to take, and decided to stay on the lee of the reef and to swim beyond the rock and around to the far side before deciding on whether to swim through.

The steeply-shelving beach means that the surf rolls almost to the shore before breaking directly downwards with great force. So you have to run in between waves, and hope to be out beyond the breaking zone before one gets you and smashes you onto the shingle like a piece of kelp ripped from a rock. Unfortunately, a couple of our group got caught and found it a bit too heavy to carry on. I timed my entrance for the little gap between the breaking of one wave and the arrival of the next, diving forwards into the approaching breaker so I'd gone through just before it broke.

Once we were heading off-shore it became much easier to swim through the rollers. You just go with them, breathe when you can, and try to stay in touch with a couple of other swimmers. As we neared the reef, I noticed that the swell had grown and was big enough to intermittently obscure the Thurlestone from view. I found it much harder to swim smoothly, and was rolled almost onto my back a couple of times. I did the usual water-swallowing, but managed not to inhale any for once. I looked up at the rock, and saw regular swimmer Maretta with her young daughter, who was out on her first wild swim and looking as though she was born in the sea, sliding through the swell like a little seal.

The sea was an opaque greeny-blue through my goggles as I swam, and when I stopped and looked at its surface it was the colour of pewter. The sun was low and partially covered by clouds; it emitted a chill light that glinted off the wavelets ahead. I swam out a little way past the rock, which was sideways on to me then, to take some photos. I tried to work out how high it is. It's probably only 30 feet or so above the sea, but somehow looks much larger. It's made up of two rock stacks that lean in towards each other and touch around fifteen feet above the sea. There is a fissure running vertically from the point where the leg stacks meet. The rock is dark and jagged with a texture like bark on an ancient oak, and its outline is broken further by the silhouetted sea birds that cling to its summit – cormorants and gulls with beaks pointing skywards.

I swam back to the other swimmers, and looked over towards the hole that was just visible at an angle. The waves, some around six feet high, were smashing into the stack nearest the shore at an angle, splatting spume across the rough surface like whipped egg-whites. The crazy angles of the sea made the arch look quite menacingly mad. Pauline told me they'd decided it was too dangerous to go through, so everyone began to swim off shore-wards down the side of the reef.

I watched the waves for a bit, and looked behind to see how

quickly they were coming. Some were smaller than others, and I began to wonder whether I could make it through, and, if not, whether I could push off the far side of the arch with my legs and escape a bashing that way. 'You're thinking of going through, aren't you?' said JJ. Hmmm, yes.

There was a quick discussion. We reckoned we could make it between waves. We were now pretty close, being pushed by the swell towards the rock. 'We're already committed, let's just body-surf through' said Pauline, and so we went for it. I swam towards the nearest, offshore stack of the arch, so that if I was washed off course I might hit the gap. A wave came through and I put my head down and swam flat out through the hole, shooting out of the other side with a rush of adrenaline to find we'd made it: me, Pauline, JJ and Wee Man Martin, all laughing and shouting with the exhilaration.

I looked back, and realised we were still very close to the rock, and that there was a huge wave approaching. It hit the arch and the small rock next to it, then surged and broke over the top. The water on this side, made more turbulent by its route through the stone, foamed and churned in sympathy with our little gang of excitable swimmers. We bobbed around for a bit, took a couple of quick snaps, and swam bravely away towards the shore, over the reef.

Floating face down, I tried to see the reef garden, but the turbulent water made visibility poor. I glimpsed through the murky, pale turquoise water some pale grey rocks with swirling seaweed rooted firmly to them, but that was it garden-wise. But who could be disappointed after the fun of the swim and the crazy surf through the Thurlestone?

I managed to avoid being dumped by the surf at the shoreline, and ran for it over the shingle of small, smooth quartz pebbles to the beach. We were all high as teenagers at a rave.

'We'll have to swim it again to see the garden,' said Kirsty through a mouthful of mint tea and home-made biscuit. The Thurlestone squatted behind her in the distance, surrounded by silver sea.

The Decision
MALINDA GREEN

You only possess what you cannot lose in a shipwreck
Abu Hamid al-Ghazali, 11th century

The first time

"You don't have pockets in a swimsuit so you can't carry money and that's part of it," the child explained. Her small companion looked puzzled. "But where would you spend it?" he asked. "Don't be silly there aren't any shops in the sea," she laughed. The tide was coming in fast, shirring pebbly treasures over the sands. Such a smooth, blank canvas at the start of it all.

Years later the conversation continued. "I have a cold water immersion method," she told the young man sitting next to her on the shingly sand. "You put yourself on the other side of the decision to get in and then it's only a question of how to do it and how long it will take you to be in heaven".

The boy gazed out over the icy-looking waves. "What's best," he asked, "slowly or jumping straight in?". He was half-thinking about how to organise his stamp collection at home, a recent fine gift from an uncle.

"It depends," she replied. "If a wave crashes over you, just gasp and accept the short cut. Think of it on a scale of one to ten. At one you dip your toes in for a paddle, but instead of thinking 'Ooh that's cold' you make The Decision because you know that soon you will pass through the cold barrier and be folded into a water duvet as cosy as a rock pool. At five you're 30 seconds away from heaven. At six you're committed to The Decision. It's made – so open your arms and embrace this salty, dashing love with all your heart. NOW YOU'RE IN and swimming through the dancing bobby dazzlers rising and rushing you up so quickly through seven, eight, nine and ten to HEAVEN. All the jigsaw pieces fall into place in this perfect space and there is nowhere in all the world you would rather be than here, now, staying afloat and alive in this heavenly moment where nothing else matters, like money or possessions."

The young philatelist looked out to sea and became immersed in the golden pathway of the sun. The Angle of Incidence directed only for his dazzled eyes. "Like here and now with me?" he asked, as The Decision is made, soft lips touch and mouths lock in limpet passion, she in the sea and he in the perfect joy of possession.

Stroke, breathe, push, sweep, roll, turn, warm, ripple, chop, kick, swirl, dip, tweeze, twist, squint, lick, nipple, press, stick, fold, return to the drawer of memory with the other albums.

The lifetime

On such a hot day others were content to stay on the beach and sunbathe. No-one wanted to coax their warm bodies into the sharp icy swell of the full tide, no matter how inviting the sparkling sea. Except the young boy slipping playfully through wavelets like oiled silk, diving under his mother's floating form nearby. At the water's edge the anxious man called them in, fearful of the tide turning and taking his darlings away. The mother gathered her duckling to shore and waved to her own mother, a bobbing silver head in the distance, to swim back from heaven.

"You see this is what my Mum taught me," she explained to him again, "that when you first take your child into a cold sea you are giving them a lifetime of joy".

The last time

It was another blazing day as they drove and twisted through lanes towards the beach, hedgerows trailing honeysuckle and chittering swallows. Dipping down suddenly they were there – the sea glittering in a perfect postcard of cloudless sky, just as she'd remembered.

The tide was low and gently ebbing away over a map of memories traced in shells and seaweed. Such a complicated design of decisions made at the end of it all.

"You'll have to carry me down darling" the woman smiled. "We can leave the wheelchair". Her grandson lifted her easily. "Do you need your bag?" he asked. "No, there's nothing to buy here. The only thing to spend on this beach is time."

Triolet on the Sea Shore
ROSAMUND TAYLOR

When I wallowed in a warm rock-pool,
I let the sea in, the waves and fresh brine,
the crabs and nets in tangled green spools.
At last I swallowed the warm rock-pool
and grew huge, snapped teeth hard as jewels.
I birthed jellyfish, algal bloom, oil-shine.
When I wallowed in a warm rock-pool,
I let the sea in, the waves and fresh brine.

Shore
JEREMY PAGE

The sea here is so still
I hesitate to break the water –
as if to break might mean to fracture,
as if the sea were not the elements
it comprises but some exquisite vase
or other precious object, and I were
some barbarian, not the only human presence
on this beach at first light, too early
in the season, goaded by insomnia
and a perverse desire to shock
every sense into sudden, utter wakefulness.

Ness Cove
EMMA PUSILL

I meet him outside the zoo, where the chattering of invisible monkeys makes more sense to me than the flotsam and jetsam of my thoughts. This is the day that the boxes in my head are made real: cardboard cubes salvaged from a life that is scuppered. He knows I need the water, even though I haven't realised it myself, and he makes it so.

I can smell the dark mouth in the cliff, damp and cool in the evening sunshine. I enjoy the feeling of being swallowed by the land, descending the tunnel into its guts before being coughed out onto the shingle. I don't think I ever told him about the goose-bump pleasure I take from that. But it doesn't matter. Not much of what will never be said matters now. Not in the way that it used to.

The sun lies shipwrecked on the cliff behind us, and the shingle mourns in shadow. The last of the gold spills from the wreck, scattered over the sea a few hundred metres off shore. If we want that gold to line our pockets and make us rich we must swim to it. And we do want that.

He is pleased to be back in a wetsuit, and I am pleased to be out of one. He is faster than me, in thought and deed; I long since gave up hope of keeping up. He waits for me to catch up from time to time, then immediately swims on as I draw close. Ordinarily that would bother me, but life has been leading from the front lately and I've come to accept my place. I can't win, and losing without striving is less crushing. So I plod, he waits. I plod, he waits.

I feel the sun, suddenly, on my bare shoulders; the warmth cuts through the low tingle in my skin and stops me dead, brings me to life. I hang vertical in the water and look for him. He is less than 20 metres away but we do not close on one another. We are motionless, strung up on the sun's gibbet. He gestures to a buoy, twice as far again offshore. I nod. I know deep water and like it. And I know that he doesn't, particularly. If his head fails him I might actually win, although I know my chances are slim. A gauntlet has been thrown and he thrives on a duel. So on I plod, but this time he doesn't wait. I sight over mercurially-smooth water and see him close on the buoy; he stops short. I pick up my pace, such as it is. This is not how it usually goes, with this competitive and confounding man. I feel a nibble of something that might be worry. We are half a mile from shore, now, and I know I can't recover him that far.

I reach him, and stop. We tread water almost nose to nose. The buoy is a body length away. "After you," he says, and gestures like a nobleman. My worry abates and I realise that even when he doesn't win, he wins. I touch the buoy, a piece of theatre that releases a tide of words. We scull, and float, and talk. There is not much laughing. His recent failure washes through him more strongly than I had suspected. The dark and the cold and the fear still flood him and I do not think the tide of that will turn soon. The tide of my failure has already turned, and the cardboard cubes waiting in what will tomorrow cease to be my home testify to it. He thinks wrongly I have somehow taken charge of my failure and rid myself of it; he tells me he is proud of me for that, and envious. I try to explain that the tide simply turned when it could advance no further, I have no control over it. His eyes turn blank. I am not sure whether he is not listening, or whether he doesn't want to hear.

When the gold has turned liquid and evaporated, taking our words with it, we strike back to the shingle. There will be more talking, when we are warm and dry and have been transported back to the light on the other side of the cliff.

There will be rum, and release, and the failures will ebb, for a while. There will be laughter, plenty of it. But for now we stand, silently wrapped in towels. In transition between the wet and dry, sea and land, failure and future.

Agnes & the Finman
ANNA KISBY

Our first swim. I hang back – he dives in,
flips off legs, shape-shifts and pulls me
under. I am tangled in flippers, gill-kissed,
forget the protest of my bones, the shock-cold
of an Orkney sea that wakes for him and glitters
gold like pagan coins thrown into wells for wishes.
Even the virgin's-veil blue of the sky is on his side
for as we loop and star-shape, my feet touching fins,
the clouds unscroll, become terrible angels
beating vast wings, decreeing *Thou Shalt Love!*
and in this light I'll sign up blind to whatever religion
he is offering, swallow salt and be cured
by the stroke of his swim, by his selkie-skin,
say *I do* blinking into the undoable knot of the sun.

Swimming at Trollhagen
MARY LOWERSON

60 degrees North light skims & glances
on and on across the fjord, ringing in the ear as music
dancing from Trollhagen & back again –
perhaps Grieg heard this summer light as sound,
caught the rhythm of the waves.

Sjórinn Freistar*
EMMA BEYNON

This storm shakes off the rest,
a high pitched whining gale.
On the nose, whipping up short hard waves.
The boat lurches, heavy going,
reef down, tighten the tiller.

The Denmark Straits, a verdant gutter,
teeming with halibut and sunken trawlers.
A Carribean blue, chill enough to cradle ice.

This storm thumps the life out of the weak,
plaiting up the guts, poisoning mouths,
until the body curls up, dreams of swimming.
Each purr of water bubbling up against the porthole,
an invitation to dive in, float, dissolve
into the release of the wind battered sea.

* *Sjórinn freistar* – Icelandic phrase: the temptation of the sea.
  In Iceland it is said that fishermen can become so tormented with
  seasickness they throw themselves into the raging waves.

Skarðsvík, West Iceland
TOM HALL

A beach like this must be swum off.

Driving along a finger of land at the end of Iceland's Snaefellsnes peninsula, past lighthouses and through a landscape of moss-covered volcanic rock, I park up by the strip of golden beach at Skarðsvík. Here the waters of Breiðafjördur meets the Greenland Sea. The road, like the ever-receding trails on Benbecula or Lewis, ribbons on towards the lighthouse at Öndverðarnes, the north-western tip of the peninsula. I stop here, and slightly self-consciously take off my socks and shoes, then head towards the water.

The tip of Snaefellsnes is not deserted, but the tourism boom that celebrates geysers and waterfalls further south is getting here more slowly. Leave the main road around the peninsula and you're almost alone. The soundtrack is the calls of seabirds, persistent wind and your own tunes. Maybe Cocteau Twins fit best.

I am here for less than two days, fulfilling a teenage promise to myself to come to Iceland, to walk among its waterfalls and green mountains. The now-not teenage me was keen on a swim as close to the Arctic Circle as I'd ever been and packed trunks accordingly.

Swimming in Iceland for locals and visitors is about hot pots, thermally-heated town pools and, above all, being in warm water underneath cold air. What I had in my head was a swift plunge into cold blue water. This beach, the only strand of golden sand I'd seen anywhere, is the place for it. I wasn't the only person to take a liking to being here. The skeleton of a Viking warrior was found buried on this beach in the 1960s. He got to hang out here for all eternity, with the mist-covered

Westfjords across the water, itself home to orcas, dolphins and sperm whales.

As lovely to look at as it is, Skarðsvík is not somewhere anyone is swimming today. My usual swimming hole is the Men's Pond at Highgate, London, but here there's no happy hubbub of fellow eccentrics ready for their dips with me, just a couple in matching Icelandic jumpers staring out to sea and a photographer setting up a tripod. His look as I stride past tells me I am ruining his picture. Of more immediate concern than that, an audience means that I am also committed, with no hope left of quietly abandoning the whole swimming idea and going back to the car. Another vehicle arrives and its passengers zip up their jackets. The wind has kicked up a little more insistently.

A beach like this, I repeat to myself, *must be swum off.* Even this far north, on a windy, cloudy afternoon, with the temperature some way off double figures.

And though at times like this a swimmer is a fish out of water I continue with the endeavour. I am the lone fruitcake walking purposefully with a towel, awkwardly stripping off out of sight yet still caught in the act. My company stares as I take equally confident paces towards the water. To everyone else, I imagine, it was very clear where I was from. At moments like this I wear English eccentricity like an invisible wetsuit.

The walk to the water's edge is both long and short. Two feet in, then up to calves. Water laps around the top of my legs. The sand shelves steeply away. Undignified dive-flop.

Bang!

The cold sting of the water is an instant hit. Though the waves are not strong I lose concentration for an instant before routine reactions kick in, and I breathe fast and swim fast parallel to the shore, then diagonally away from it. After a minute or two I am more comfortable, halfway through my planned hundred strokes.

Turning for home and looking back to land from the water the golden sand is framed perfectly by dark rocks on one side and a small cliff on the other. Far beyond the beach but dominating the view Snaefellsjokull glacier gleams, capped with brilliant snow and a white cloud. It is an unexpected and thrilling sight. I had not seen it until this point and yet here it is, no longer hiding in the cloud that had obscured it. Between it and this tiny, hidden strand of yellow there is nothing else for miles. A unique view, from a vantage point that is the swimmer's alone.

The sight of the vast mountain roots me instantly in where I am. Yesterday I wasn't in Iceland. Tomorrow I will be on my way to America. Right now I am right here. And getting cold. Then I am out of the frigid water with the hurry of someone who has just been in it, and into the silence of now-still air, and then drying and changing quickly behind the rock. From here back into the normal world – if such a thing exists in Iceland – where I could pass myself off as anyone else, with the secret of sand between my toes for the rest of the day.

At Ólafsvík, a small town down the road, I stop for cake and hot chocolate. Seeing me shivering the waitress asked what I had been doing. 'People in Iceland don't do that,' she smiles. Who would not relish hearing such a gentle admonishment, and take it as confirmation of a slightly dotty mission accomplished?

There are many wonders to be found exploring Iceland, together with the nagging sense that far more are hiding just out of reach. The dark, cold water yielded something. At Skarðsvík, more than anywhere else I find on this incredible island, is a secret grudgingly revealed.

Selma and Ture
JANE GREENE PETTERSSON

Selma finished the row she was on. She didn't need to look, she had already turned the heel of the sock and was heading towards the toe. Then drop one stitch for each of the four needles until the sock narrowed down ready to be sewn up. She had been knitting socks for over seventy years and the familiarity was comforting.

She could feel the warmth of the sun letting go where she sat on the veranda although it would still be up until around midnight at this time of year. Her sight was going. The doctors said you couldn't operate on a green cataract. Ture was worse. He had a bit of vision at the side, nothing in the front. They had a lifetime of working outside in the long bright summer days, on the fields, setting potatoes, cutting hay and out at sea laying out the nets, bringing in the fish. The winters were long and dark and maybe in the old days their blue Nordic eyes would have been rested during the dark months with only the yellow light of candles and oil lamps to trouble them and early to bed so as not to waste money. Now the electric light could burn bright all night and their eyes, adapted like the pale eyes of a wolf to let in as much light as possible, were over used by the time they grew old. You couldn't shoot the wolves now. Directive from Brussels.

There was no place undiscovered in Selma and Ture's house. No step would rise suddenly to trip them up. Everything was familiar. The loss of sight was not such a great hindrance.

They said that the Baltic was not like other seas. It was gentler, not so salty, its own kinds of weeds and fish. It was where Selma had learned to swim. Selma and the other children taught themselves to swim. They used one of the smaller pieces of cut timber from the saw mill as a float until they were good enough to swim without it.

The thing was to be the first one in. Sometimes there was still ice floating on the water, and it would just be a dip. Down in the freezing, blue green water, then out again, laughing, breathless, triumphant. You had to watch out for the terns guarding their nests on the little island just out from the jetty. They would swoop down and peck your head if you got too close.

They always had fish to eat, even when times were hard and there wasn't much else. All the children learned to lay out the nets and pull them up again the next morning, hoping for something worth eating.

Ture should be back by now. He was out with the nets. Even though he couldn't see, even though their sons said he shouldn't go anymore, that he was too old.

"One day he won't come back Mum. He'll fall in."

But what would Ture do if he didn't go out with the boat in the summer time, sit at home and watch the television?

Every evening in summer he set off on his bike; across the road listening for traffic then straight down to the harbour. The saw mill was long gone now, but they still found batons of wood washed up at the shore, smooth from years washed by the waves and under the ice in the winter.

Ture knew the shape of the bay, he could hear the echo along the shore, hear how the sound of the engine changed. He could feel weight of the fish in the nets.

Their sons wanted them to move up to the village, to the sheltered housing. Supposed to be very nice inside and they had their own sauna that you could use once a week although some of them had refugees living there now. Women with covered heads and serious looking young men from Afghanistan and Iraq but that didn't bother Selma. Her own mother would never have gone into town without a headscarf tied under her chin. Her father had gone to work far away in Canada when the saw mill closed down and work was scarce. He sent money home but he came back to fight the Russians in the winter war. One thing they were used to here was winter.

Selma put the sock back into her knitting basket. Ture was late. Best go and look for him. No point bothering anyone else. It was a while since she had been down to the sea but the path was as familiar as the feel of the woollen sock in her hands.

The sun grew gentle. She sat on the big rock to rest. There was a tiny thread of anxiety inside her now. What if Ture didn't come back? Maybe she should swim out to meet him. She could be like that girl on the news, swimming the refugees to safety. They said she was in the water for three hours, pulling the boat. No that was madness. Then they really would put her away. But the summer would be over soon. This might be the last time, the last swim.

She took off her clothes and laid them on the rock where they would not get wet. The water was not cold and the sand was firm under her feet. She waded in up to her knees then up to her waist. She felt the water rush up inside her where they had taken everything away after the last child was born. Selma loved to swim and she was a strong swimmer. Why had she left it so long? She stretched out and let the water carry her off her feet. She flipped over onto her back and let her hair flow out behind her. Then in the distance she heard the thrum of an outboard motor. Ture was coming back.

Galway Blues
TIM MARTINDALE

It was May, in Galway. The grey horizon rose with the swelling sea and the ground was sinking. Wind and rain lashed at my trouser legs, while land and sea were merging into one watery plane. I stood on the promenade transfixed by the famine memorial: the story of the starving young girl who had walked to Galway City from her rural home inland, only to die a few days later; the sea captains who volunteered to sail the first famine relief boats to America. Hard to imagine the bravery and self-sacrifice needed to set across that vast ocean, as I peered into the heaving grey, trying to make out the smudge of Inis Oirr, the smallest of the Aran Islands.

I was relieved to be back on the mainland after walking that island's ragged edge the day before. A sense of desolation had come upon me and I understood how profoundly difficult solitude can be. Confronted with it and unable to escape for the day, I had been overwhelmed by an anxiety that was nauseating, as if I might be swallowed up by the sea, the grey sky and stone. *Why had I come here?* Yet as I walked further out towards the western edge of the island to where the surf curled and broke heavily on the shore, the sea a deep shade of Atlantic blue, I felt a growing sense of peace and acceptance. I lay on a large flat rock near a rusting shipwreck and the lighthouse that failed to save it, and listened to the surf. Nothing between that rock and America except a great ocean and I imagined the hope, longing and kinship Irish emigrants and their families must have felt when they gazed across those waters. The rock that held and cradled me was a comfort in the midst of awe. The salty air was like oxygen for my soul and the lighthouse and distant cliffs of Connemara were strangely familiar – reminiscent of my native Cornwall. I felt a deep longing for home.

After a restless, wind-harried night in a B&B, I'd caught the morning ferry back to the mainland and now found myself traipsing the seafront, hoping to immerse myself in Irish waters before departing for Dublin and then home the following day. Despite the bleakness of the promenade, I felt oddly at home walking towards the swimming terraces and diving platforms where I intended to take my swim. Often had I walked in all weathers along Penzance promenade in Mount's Bay, to the Victorian lido and wilder swims off Battery Rocks, seeking a sea in which to lose and find myself again.

Soaked through by yet another squall of rain I almost turned back, and then ahead I saw one, then two swimmers bravely enter the water – then a third! They plunged in like penguins despite the strong wind and heavy swell. The sight of these brave souls defying the weather lifted my heart and my determination was renewed.

I joined another swimmer shedding clothes and donning trunks on the terrace whilst more and more swimmers arrived on the scene, or emerged from the small changing room. One waddled, walrus-like, in wetsuit, flippers, hat, goggles and webbed gloves. "Where is the Man from Atlantis going today then?" a lady in a stripy swimsuit called after him. He smiled and waved with the aura of an explorer who might not return, before stepping off the platform and into the sea. I followed quickly, descending the steps and launching myself into the bracing sea, feeling the swell take and lift my body, threatening for an instant to hurl me back against the concrete. *Have faith*, I told myself, as I propelled myself out and away. The water was cold and choppy, but joyous. I swam only a little way before turning back, wishing to conserve energy in case the conditions made exiting the water difficult. Yet I felt that I had finally arrived in Ireland, in body and spirit.

In the small shelter where men were gathering to change and get dry (the women braving the elements outside), I was enfolded by the warmth of aging but spirited swimmers exchanging news in lilting west coast Irish. They came there every day of the year, one told me, no matter the weather, and swore that it never failed to cure the blues. I thought about all the swimmers up and down the archipelago, linked by this brave and simple activity that defies the despondency and anxiety of everyday modern life; this immersive experience that anchors body and mind in the present moment and connects us to the elements and the seas around us from which we draw our being and are restored on a deeply physical level; how central water has been to my own formation of self, sense of place and home.

Afterwards, walking back along the promenade – damp, chilled, but fully alive – the weather was beginning to lift and so too had my despondency. The lighthouse and rusting ship wreck on Inis Oirr stood in my mind's eye, signs on a path stretching along the Atlantic edge and into my past and future.

I remembered what nature writer Richard Mabey said about being away from the landscape that shaped you as a young person, that it sometimes takes a 'metaphorical junction' to connect that place with those you journey through later. Perhaps swimming will – like writing – be one way I connect my inner and outer territories, and find a way to be at home in the world.

Sundays at Rachel Finlayson
REBECCA ROUILLARD

When it comes to wild swimming in South Africa the options are truly wild – sometimes even life threatening. As a child it was drummed into me to be sensible in the sea and always follow the rules: only swim where there are shark nets, swim between the red flags, listen to the lifeguards' whistles, don't go past the backline, beware of rip currents, respect the sea – never turn your back on it. I experienced those moments when you come up for air only to have a wave break in your face; a mouth and nose full of saltwater. I knew what it felt like to be tumbled under a wave, how terrifying it is when you lose track of which way the surface is.

Even swimming inland requires a sense of adventure. I once fell off a jetty into the St Lucia Estuary – home to crocodiles and hippos. I was warned about swimming in standing or sluggish water – there could be bilharzia. I once got covered in leeches while swimming at Forest Falls in Mpumalanga. Even taking a break from a family hike to swim in the icy mountain streams of the Drakensberg created a certain frisson – other hikers might come across us swimming in our underwear. But the world's largest open water swim, the Midmar Mile, takes place in the relatively safe environment of a dam.

At age eleven I decided, in conversation with a new friend, that I was going to swim the Midmar Mile. Hannah had wispy blonde hair and a round face with dimples. I'd always wanted dimples. She played the cello, her parents were divorced – still relatively unusual in my school – and she was unfailingly nice. At the beginning of standard five, Hannah and I, with eleven-year-old intensity, became best friends. We sent in our entry forms and began training in January for the Midmar Mile in March.

Every Sunday afternoon one of our parents would drive me and Hannah down to Durban beachfront and drop us off at the Rachel Finlayson Pool; a fifty-metre saltwater lido, named after the 1928 Olympic coach and 'mother' of South African swimming. The floor and walls of the pool were tiled in dark blue, the lane markings stark white in contrast, and it was always inexplicably empty. It seemed that people preferred the beach. Every Sunday we swam exactly 34 lengths. (A mile is 33 lengths and we'd round that up to finish on the same side of the pool we started from.)

I sang snatches of songs while I swam, sometimes just one phrase over and over: *Herring boxes without topses, sandals were for Clementine*, fragments of words bubbling out of my mouth with each breath.

At first the water was a barrier I had to tear apart with cupped hands – a birth of sorts – but then I would find my rhythm and I was flying, soaring through the water.

When we'd finished our 34 lengths we pulled our clothes on over our damp costumes and bought an ice cream at Milky Lane while we waited for our lift home; a soft serve dipped in chocolate sauce and peanuts – the chocolate hardening to a crisp shell.

The start of the Midmar Mile was notoriously scary – you were likely to get kicked, scratched, pulled, pushed under. We'd psyched ourselves up for it, Hannah and I. There was an air horn blast and I ran, elbows out, over slippery mud into a thrashing mass of swimmers, each trying to clear just a small area of water in front of them. I lost track of Hannah immediately. I pushed and swam until there was actually space to swim, until I could find my rhythm, breathe.

I swam, I sang. There were no lengths to count so I sighted the huge inflatable buoys that mark the course, and, when it was close enough, I sighted the finish line on the far bank of the dam. It seemed like I'd been swimming all day but the end got steadily bigger until eventually the water was shallow enough for me to stand. I waded and then jogged through the mud, up a concrete boat ramp and over the finish line. My family found me there, in amongst hundreds of other swimmers, and photographed me with my medal, embarrassed and triumphant.

Later I found Hannah and her family. *Where were you? I looked for you...* it turned out that Hannah didn't make it past the start, she panicked in the churning crush, put her hand up and someone in a boat pulled her out of the water. All that training, all those Sunday afternoons – she didn't even make ten metres, let alone a mile. She wasn't tough enough, but I was.

I lost touch with Hannah when we went to high school and then my family moved to another town.

Sometime later I read in the newspaper that Hannah's stepmother and sister had been killed in a car accident. Hannah's dad was also injured but he survived; Hannah had not been in the car.

The following year, in an article about the school art exhibition, I found a photo of a painting by Hannah. She'd painted her sister curled into a foetal position, asleep under the ground, calla lilies blooming all around her, at peace. It was a beautiful, heart-breaking painting, a confident piece. I was surprised that it was so good; she was better than I remembered from our art lessons. Her tragedy had made her into an artist. I was envious of Hannah, not of the awful thing that happened, but envious of her certainty – the clarity of her vision. I cut the picture out and saved it.

Two-thirds of Our World is Ocean
REDFERN BARTON

Sussex. An overcast August day. In the post-war gloom two children shiver on a pebble beach below towering cliffs, the wind off the sea whipping them. Urged by their father – a very keen swimmer – they tentatively test the sea, trying to enjoy the experience, splashing each other and shouting. Their father swims far out, his head a dark dot in the distance; their mother unsettled and anxious until his return. Later they struggle to remove their trunks modestly under rough towels. Sea kale among the stones; thrift and harebells in the short turf on the cliff top.

Brittany. Teenage friends walk through the pine forest to the wide beach, the air scented with resin, sand soft between their toes. The light-filled air is bright, the sea sparkling, small waves dance in the shimmer. This water is shallow and warm, silk on the skin. It's a revelation that the sea can give pleasure like this. Joy and disbelief that the water is not fighting you here, it invites you in. Soon he takes it for granted. On balmy evenings they buy warm pancakes from a beach shack. Windbreak tamarisk hedges with tiny pink flowers. Pots of carefree geraniums.

The Riviera. Five summers later. The South of France, too hot and glamorous for serious swimming. Lazy strokes of a leisurely crawl to reach a floating platform conveniently sited not too far out. He pulls himself onto it and lies in the sun and then dives sleekly to impress an unbelievably beautiful girl lounging nearby. Her boyfriend – jealous perhaps – challenges him to race back. A fast competitive crawl, thrashing the sea. In the late afternoon climbing slowly up narrow half-shaded alleys to the apartment; bougainvillea and the scent of jasmine.

The Gorges de Verdon. Sleep in a wooden hut above the canyon and wake before dawn to see the sun rise at Pointe Sublime. At midday they swim in the cold river far below. The summer stream flows steady, bordered by meadows of long waving grass; but they are wary. Unseen storms in the mountains could cause an avalanche of terrifying water to rush down suddenly without warning, through the gorges, fast and deep and dangerous. Each of them swims in the icy water – a vigorous butterfly stroke to warm himself. This is not a place to relax. Yellow kingcups in the water margin and further back vineyards, the grapes too sour to eat.

Canada. Lakes, icy snow water, so clear that each pebble is visible. Tiny fish. It is immensely deep. A child falls in and the men rescue him. Almost a tragedy. Apple orchards.

Hong Kong. The pool is fenced and the metal gate clangs shut as she comes in. Bright butterflies, big as the palm of her hand, skim the surface to drink like swallows. It's early; few people awake. Later the humid air will be unbearable so she always swims now, self-conscious breaststroke, swan-like, wanting his gaze, languid and sensual. She is half his heart, as he is half hers. Swimming below the surface she comes up suddenly to tease him, laughing where he stands on the edge, solemn in his city suit, longing for her. She is a golden seal, sun browned, her hair swept back from her forehead by the water, minute droplets on her skin, brown eyes shining – perfect to him. Hibiscus and frangipani by the gate. Flame trees in the city.

Australia. Christmas Day on Whale Beach. The house perches on the hillside, its verandah peering over the bay. They all insist on swimming before lunch and take the path down, brushing through wide-leaved banana trees and palm fronds. A girl wears a grass skirt; the younger boys run on ahead. A rectangular sea water pool, built at one end of the beach, is refreshed at high tide when large waves come crashing over. There, elderly people with crocodile suntans can totter in safety. The sea is exhilarating but strange; it seems to belong more to the surfers who understand how to play with it properly. Last week at Manly Beach there were steel anti-shark nets.

Near East, Middle East, Far East. Hotel pools, tepid with chemicals. Security men, uniformed and armed, look down like voyeurs from roof tops, guarding Western guests. How can you swim in circumstances like these? In manicured gardens, gardenias and stephanotis.

Greece. A bay in the Peloponnese. Three women in a small sailboat. Two of them frolic in the water while the third trims the boat. She calls out casually that the sea below them is more than a thousand metres deep and local fishermen have seen sharks. The two girls fly back into the boat. It's a very long way down. He hears about this later – and about the dolphins that accompany them in the evening on the homeward journey. Rosemary and juniper, myrtle and thyme on the dry hills.

Sussex. An old pool surrounded by trees, a turquoise jewel, wide and beautiful, almost at the end of the town. A secret suntrap. The turnstile clucks quietly as he passes through, alone these last years. He dives into the deep end. Icy shock. Skin retracts, he breathes in sharply. He loves this place – swimming in fresh spring water. Four lengths of front crawl, energetic, blood pulsing. No longer young, the cold makes his heart laugh, makes him feel alive and vigorous. Someone greets him but it's difficult to hear under water and the filters are gurgling. Sunlight casts his shadow onto the bottom, accompanying him like a watchful sea creature. Tiring now, he turns on his back looking up at the morning sky, pale, scored with widening contrails, like the wayward doodles of a bored designer. Early travellers up there, airborne; he down here, content, water-borne, his arms in slow turbine backstroke. It's going to be another very hot day. Behind the wall the Corsican pines are whispering.

PATRICK TAGGART

Fish leave no fin prints,
no tracks across the ocean.
Be water, my heart.

River

Spitchwick
LYNNE ROPER

Honey and I popped over to Spitchwick this morning. It's a warmish autumn day, with a slightly chill breeze. There's still some heat in the sun which pops out occasionally from behind puffy, greying clouds illuminating the ponies grazing on the common by the river. We can smell their gorgeous, horsey scent and, in Honey's case, the mouth-watering whiff of tottering heaps of steaming dung.

It's 11 degrees in the water today, so I decide on a wetsuit because I want to swim for at least thirty minutes. As I enter the river down the stone 'steps', I notice a dipper who performs his jerky little dance from a rock by the island before dipping under the water, then zipping away downstream. His cream bib makes his low-level flight visible for a little while. Honey potters around in the shallows, then swims across and back. I can hear her breathing in little puffs as she passes.

The water today is mirror-black on the far side. The leaves on the trees behind are turning and their full height is reflected as though soaked into the water. On the near side I can see coppery patches here and there, but for the most part the gravelly bottom has been obliterated by huge drifts of autumn leaves and twiggy debris from last month's stormy weather. The leaves blacken as they decompose, and the newer ones – orange, greeny-yellow and tan – glow randomly through the peaty water like jewels, flashing in the current. When I step in, I sink to my ankles in the spongy layer then slide to the side as my foot hits a hidden rock. It's safer to just swim, so I leap forwards and plunge straight under before turning to head upstream against the current on the far side, where it's deep.

The water of the Double Dart smells and tastes of the moors:

chill, fresh, pure and peaty. I swim in front crawl to warm up, and the water beneath me is black as night. Silver bubbles arc from my hands, which glow disembodied through the water in an eerie, copper light. Icy rivulets push through the neck of my suit and down my back like shivers from a ghost story. And then it hits: full-on ice-cream head for the first time since the spring. I try to swim through, but have to stop so I float on my back, arms outstretched, in a cross. The pain in my forehead subsides and I can hear only my amplified breathing in my submerged ears. Blue sky, clouds, oak trees, and the edge of a backlit cloud. I begin to turn in the current and stay there for a while, before swimming again. After the third go, the ice-cream head is no more so I carry on upstream, then back down at four times the pace, then a float around, then back up and down till I start to feel cold again.

I can hear Honey growling and barking from the bank, and stand up to watch her. Her hair is soaked and curling, and she's charging around the common in a zig-zag pattern with a stick in her mouth. Occasionally she tosses and catches the stick, arse and loopy tail waving, having a big, doggy laugh. I love that a wild swim affects my dog in the same way that it affects me, or maybe we're both just crazy bitches?

On the walk back I notice that a crone of a crab apple tree, bearded with lichens, has shed her load of pale yellow fruit. We stop and I pick them up in my towel, leaving the ones that lie in horse-shit for Honey, who is partial to a windfall apple or ten. She tries one but declines the rest, possibly because they're a little sour, or because the horse poo is not fresh enough, like sour cream.

Gazing up at the tree, I see a sprinkling of crab apples still clinging to the branches and looking, against the greeny-grey lichen, like a fruity tiara on a tipsy granny at a barn dance. The music of the river fades as we walk away.

River Swimming
WAYNE TENYSON

I

Your face, laughter, the blue sky
And the fast river water
Over pebbles and dark stones.
We took turns to be with you

Or to swim. And now and then
We were all sat there alone
In the shade under the umbrella
Separate and together.

To go from the heat of the sun
Into the swift mountain water
Bring back the bottle cooled
In the shallows, weighed with a rock

What else have we got?
Might you remember sharing
This day, late September
Or will I have to tell you

About the swift stream
And leaves on the current
And how we swam
And lay together

As the shadows lengthened.

II

Late afternoon and the day turned
Towards evening and to autumn
We sat at the bar.
A new winter coat and hat
A man on crutches and a game of cards
The fire unlit since last winter.

III

A black dog on the street
Of the small town as we drove through
And later swam in the cold river
By the bridge with bullet holes
Held an apple for you to smell
Placed your forehead in the bend of my nose
And you laughed.

Cloud Chamber
JANET SUTHERLAND

in a new light   the river
water weightier
than oil or slub
viscous slip
beer-bottle brown

you notice don't you
language clarifies

or chant these slim diminutives:
rivulet rill run burn beck
runnel freshet torrent force jet
and riveret (now rare or obsolete)

none of them hold
  such corrugations welded from below
  such heavy fish
etched as with acid from cast steel
these gate-keeper
herons   iron posts
charting a route
you might well walk beside

bright air above
cloud trails   scraps   gnats   slant swifts in flight

Buoyed By The Tides
LOUISA THOMSEN BRITS

The water, graphite-dark and edged with silver light, flows beneath the jetty. Church bells strike quarter past midnight. In this arc of time between dusk and dawn, the landscape whispers an unfamiliar night language about mystery, pause and passion. There is invisible rustling and stirring around the river like a wakeful lover rippling bedclothes in the dark. The full moon catches the undulations of the water and highlights my fear of its depth and caprice.

We light a lantern, leave its small flicker of warmth on the jetty to guide us and step into the river as the incoming tide reaches its peak. Swimming in the dark reveals a viscosity to the water and distorts our knowledge of this familiar place. The bulk of a flint barn seems to soak up the light. A bramble-covered fence that slides down the riverbank into the water sits like a crouched and silent figure. And the wooden uprights of the jetty loom like gallows above us. But we are absorbed by the illicit pleasure of swimming in the silken water that eddies around us, carrying dark bronze weed and a taste of the open sea.

For a few minutes, we dwell in silence and intimacy with the touch of the water. Then looking up from the centre of the dark river, I see a single shooting star fall in a white flash. It's as if, for a second, the river has dropped its guard to receive the sky and us; as if our bodies, made up of so much water, are celebrated and welcomed to high tide. This is my reward for allowing myself to be tugged by the tides and an undercurrent of fear. I swim because I'm scared of deep water but more alarmed by the prospect of not feeling fully immersed in the immediacy and richness of life. And I swim to stay buoyant above the dark undertow of depression. Tributaries of joy and sadness flow into these moments in the Ouse. The river heightens our pleasures, dissolves our cares and carries our losses out to the sea.

We are relaxed and permeable, inhabiting a liminal place of softened perceptiveness like the space between the edge of the day and the moment of sleep. The river has called us to explore the margins, to come to the edge and wade in. Our minds grow limpid, our bodies lose their boundaries.

On misty days, the landscape has a nebulous, ghost-like beauty. We swim upstream where the sky meets the water. The river grasps at the stuff on the periphery of our lives, inviting us to consider what flows close to us, unseen but essential. The sun, suffused through thin layers of vapour, feels like something bright on the edge of our awareness.

Getting to know this watery place has unsettled our solid habits and changed habitual vision. When we shed our clothes and everyday lives and move into the depths, all our senses open us to what the river has to give – it offers us its moods and greetings and, for a few minutes at least, the possibility of a spacious and attentive life. That's why I come back here throughout the year, trying not to confuse purpose with performance. This public immersion is not a deliberate challenge. It's not about conquering the river but being in it, part of it. It's not about endurance or even the pursuit of health benefits – the calorie burn, a boost to circulation and the immune system or improved libido. But getting in the cold water lubricates the complex connections between our inner and outer worlds. In the folds of the river, my body, stretched by pregnancies and husked by time, unfurls in the elasticity and softness of the water until I feel more responsive, more receptive. In the unswervable mutability of the Ouse there's a sense of opening out, of being completely present. We've learned to observe its flow and fluctuations, anticipating the moment when it will accommodate us. We watch, wait, want and slip in. It intuitively receives, moves and lives around us without changing itself.

As we immerse ourselves in the life of the river, we see further into our own.

The fluid nature of the river, an open and communal place running through the fixedness of landscape and our domestic lives, is unifying. This interstitial space between us, and between our relentless activities and responsibilities is where we relinquish ourselves but remain held. This is a place where the human and wild converge. The tides, the dog walkers and sodden banks, the iridescent gleam of a kingfisher, the crows in ragged mourning dress and low cloud, the muscular, slick, black, smooth-backed curve of a seal, drifting woodsmoke, shrieking gulls, slender cormorant and us are all particular and all one, part of the unbroken cycle of life and death and renewal. We feel this intricate interplay from our place in the water and share a sense of deep aliveness. The shifting river claims us all and courses on through the seasons of our lives, its memory of us wavering. And we climb out, washed through and celebratory, to laugh and swear on the riverbank, too numb to dress but with a renewed commitment to embrace uncertainty and tenderly yield to everything that exists within and without.

A Swim Down River
MAT CHRISTIAN THOMAS

The river here is ten feet across, tree-lined and black in the shade. The water is always cold. The bank is steep; at a certain point he is committed. Entering a body of water is always odd, always a transition, but here the water is so dark that flighty spirits in him are disturbed with the wrongness of it.

The first few strokes are fitful. Like the first steps of baby ruminants. Wild water is most often a splash; friends dashing into frigid water – screams, laughs and then out. But this is different, this is seven miles of river alone. His chin is a prow. This is a communing. The secret is to glide.

Banks of bramble and bracken. There is no exit here. It is all part of a tunnel with the alder leaf vaulting cracked by sunlight here and there. The spots of dappled light, made compelling through contrast – some the size of fishes, others a wall mirror – are delicious to pass through. A mile in. A thin lake snaking through fields.

Dragonflies are pastoral splashes of paint on the river's canvas. They are incomparable savages in microcosm. They are the insect kin of sharks, lions and eagles. Superior in fact; the world has no better hunter. But even this close, he has no sense of this. He is charmed by them, each sighting a gift.

Cows crowd the riverbank, pushing through hedges. We lack a suitable common simile for their curiosity. They are different to sheep and pigs. Here cows form a tableaux of dull, interested faces. They have the aspect of refugees watching soldiers pass.

The river opens up. There are people now. Suddenly the river is a festival of voices. There are boats of families. Someone is always falling in crossing from boat to boat. Someone is always shouting, "How do you paddle this thing?" Someone is always calling, "Ramming Speed!" He enjoys the status of celebrity as he passes them. "Where are you going?" "Lewes." He might as well have said Alaska.

A kingfisher. A dart of tangerine and blue. It stops at a branch. They have become rare but this river, fishy and slow, is perfect. There is something about a solitary animal that amplifies the feeling of connection. He thinks perhaps kingfishers are his favourite bird. He feels its kinship. It skips past him and he turns in the water, gliding backwards to watch it go. It is gone. He would have it follow him. He would have it land in his wet hand.

He passes fishermen. Some draw in their lines. He is always worried they will object but they amongst all people seem to understand what he is doing.

A puzzle of weirs. The river shifts; it's tidal now. What was black, becomes brown. With loose calculations, he plotted that the sea would be drawing away and the running river will carry him. Fields open up around him. Houses appear on hills. The river, now moving too quickly, has less life about its body. The odd cloud of flies and below him perhaps mullet; great clumps of weeds on the banks sift fronds through the water. When he rounds a corner and sees swans he is as beguiled as he is wary. They are interested in him but let him float by. Always there are cows, bullocks, horses. Occasionally something unknown rustles in long grasses.

Out of the river for a period. A confused crisscross better walked. More people. Getting out is a chore: the mud is wet cement. Steeper banks are drier but tend to offer loose grasses and hidden thistles for handholds.

He had once taken his daughter down this river in a kayak. Racing against the lowering sun, he had decided not to try for

Lewes but to dismount here and telephone for a lift. She was five. He drew their craft to the edge of a long, wet bank and flipped his daughter into two feet of gummed mud. One hand on her, another pulling the kayak, it was a perfect coalescence of the dangerous and the hilarious into one moment. They fought through it. She was up to her hips. Both laughing, him panicked. She trusted him implicitly. By the end they had both lost their shoes at the bottom of deep black holes that held their shape only long enough to watch them be swallowed. He stashed the kayak and carried her past Hamsey church on his shoulders to a road two miles away. Their faces were brown and they smelled of peat. *Was this*, she asked her mother the next day, *the greatest adventure ever?*

The river now is as wide as an arm's throw. In a field, old farm machinery – suited to bygone tasks – that will never move again. Tired now, he notices how the flow of the river has dropped. The cold waters are stilled by the inward flow of the sea perhaps eight miles away. And then it turns finally, becomes brackish and slowly heads the other way. He gets out on the right. This is the end. It is sadness, relief and gentle triumph in one moment.

It is a thing to see a river pouring the wrong way. An uncommon rush to the higher ground. Hard to imagine that the tide, edging inward, can push so hard. But the sea is vast, the river little, and that slow drawing in squeezed between two banks of grey mud exercises great vitality northwards. The river is a line drawn in the sand on a coastal plain filled and unfilled every day with salted breath.

On the bus home, the sun has mostly dried him. He smells uncommon but not bad, like a man whose work is clearly physical but difficult to discern. The river is all about him. It tightens his skins as it dries.

The Ripple
SEEMA KAPILA

As a long line of children and adults, they moved slowly, snake like, through the open fields. Having left the campsite in shimmering heat it made sense to go under cover, towards the woods. This troupe had camped together for nearly fourteen summers and had slowly learnt to live with less; a quiet farmer's field, an open fire which was never put out, and somewhere near to get drinking water and use the toilet.

She walked upright at the back of the line, making sure her feet were firm on the ground. Covering her shoulders with a thin blue shawl to keep the sun off, the delicate silver embroidery sparkled in the haze. This summer she was determined to walk proud, nomadic in attitude, simplifying her relationship with the modern world.

Once into the woods the air changed. Green coolness brought relief. Sluggishness slowly shifted into quicker movements as the children picked up sticks. Adult talk became livelier.

Then the joy of seeing the river. It was only a small trickle of a thing but cool water nevertheless to put hot feet into. The human snake slithered towards the river bank. Some of the children took off their shoes and stepped carefully down onto the sharp stones while others, who had sandals on, explored with more confidence further upstream. She walked in quietly, barefoot. The cold fresh water tickled between her toes and it felt wonderful. She instantly breathed in and then out, reconnecting.

The water set running strong memories of a previous year when the whole group had come across a large, private spring-fed lake on one of their hot afternoon walks. It was situated in a clearing north of the campsite. A small wooden jetty floated out onto its blue-green surface with trees and bushes brushing around it on all sides. One of the older girls spotted it and announced that she was definitely going in. Her enthusiasm soon created a ripple through the rest of the group and one by one, gently egging each other on, they had all got in; the smallest ones on their parents' shoulders. They all enjoyed their first wild swimming experience together until the owner spotted them and gave them only a few minutes to "clear off". Although she had been the last to enter the water and was not as confident as some, the experience had moved her. This small herd of humans had bathed together in the open air, laying claim to a natural watering hole that had cleared and rejuvenated their minds and bodies.

Once out of the small river and onwards through the woods her feet continued to tingle. She loved the energising effect of the running water. Recently on two remote holidays she had been compelled and brave enough to sit in a fast flowing river cushioned in a carefully chosen natural pool, letting the water flow all around her; the sound of the rushing bubbles drowning out all other noises and thoughts. It was cleansing. It was healing. She was quietly grateful. And after, when she had dried herself off, she felt more alive, more upright, and free.

It is customary for many Indians, whenever and wherever they see water – "pani" – to bless it and, better still, get in. Her own father would wade with his thin and bony flamingo-like legs, trousers rolled up, into the sea at Bournemouth for his yearly "puja dip", his worshipful dunk to the oneness.

Back now at the dry campsite she sat under the cool cloth awning to plan with others the walk for tomorrow. It would pass by another small river and possibly a larger one that they could all try and swim in. Hopefully with no owner around they would be free to enjoy the water and have some fun.

She gazed out past the open fields and the campfire towards the distant hills, listening to the bubbly sound of the children chasing each other like dragonflies with water guns and cups of water. They were all waiting for the sun to dip slightly so that the evening festivities could rightly begin. She would then look up at the dark blue night sky with all its stars and see it as a vast sea of openness.

eeeooo

MARK BRIDGE

"Smile!", she calls. I lose concentration and blink as my head breaches the surface of the water. It doesn't really matter, of course, but I'm annoyed with myself. Warm air catches the back of my throat. I imagine the sunlight blistering the back of my neck as punishment for... for what? For failing to perform in a family show that no-one wants to see. Synchronised open-water swimming. No tickets, no times and often no audience. "Smile like you mean it!" Mothers always want the best for their children, don't they? That's what I keep telling myself. I don't understand why we need to practise so much but I trust. The others tell me that belief comes before understanding. Maybe I'm on some kind of spiritual journey, waiting for revelation. Am I holy already? Born of mud? Begotten, not created? "Show me your teeth!" Mother's voice cuts through my dreaming again. It's not a request. This is a command. I bare my lips. The result feels more like a grimace but from a distance I'm sure the effect is still the same. "I'm smiling now" I call back. That's not what I want to say. What I want to say is "For god's sake, mother, I'm an eel. We always smile. It's what we do. Even when men hunt us and we swallow their hooks down to our bellies." Funny how it's usually men tugging at our entrails. I don't say any of this, of course. But just look at me. A face made for smiling and a body that's... well... sleek. Sleeeeek. Oh, we love the vowels. They suit our mouths. Eeeeeel. Ooooouse. What? Of course we named the river. Ouse means 'water'. And don't give me any of that 'slippery as an eel' talk, either. We're not all criminals. Sinuous, never slimy, Mother says. I blame the dolphins for our bad press. Stupid buggers. They do the formation swimming thing too, but they're all about the audience. Stick 'em in a paddling pool and they'll keep performing. Put an eel in the bath and it's out through the overflow before you can say "Finding Nemo". And yet it's the dolphins you love, you landpeople, marvelling at their talent for showing off. You buy tuna that's described as 'dolphin friendly'. Dolphin-friendly tuna. Like you think tuna is an aquatic labrador, wagging its idiot tail in greeting as a dolphin swims past. But eel, the mysterious genius eel, we're novelty cookery ingredients. Smoked, sliced and served with a poached egg. A duck egg, for the love of god. What sort of perversity is that? Surely somewhere there's an Old Testament rule that tells grown men not to play with their food. Yes, men again. Not that I don't identify as male but I'd rather enjoy an eel body in all its glistening, phallic glory rather than seeing it dissected on buttery toast. So I smile. I look like I'm enjoying myself. And I'm honestly not sure if I am. All I can say is I'm built for it. Swimming and smiling. It seems natural. But, truth be told, it's like asking if I enjoy breathing. For me, for us, to live is to smile. Eee.

The First Thing, Always, is the Cold
HANNAH LINDEN

how it reintroduces my toes
and needle points of shock at groin
and nipples, before I, finally,
risk shoulders and back
of head. Then words become
meaningless. Everything I need
to hold myself upright, slides
fluid and through. Down and in
replace up, on; and forward
is a belonging. Wisdom
is an eel finding its way back
from the Sargasso Sea; wealth
the way sunlight splits upwards
to surface like gold through diamond.

Locomotion
TARA GOULD

In a clearing between trees on the banks of the River Lugg in Wales, a small group of people were gathered, supine on faded towels. Close by, a large black dog and a red haired girl sat beside an old woman in a wheelchair. The woman's grey hair stuck to her sweaty forehead, the black dog was panting, and the child was still dripping from her recent swim; a lime ribbon of water weed stuck to her pale back. The three were observing the river intently, as if waiting for something to appear.

The girl, Connie, was watching the Water Treadmill; a bed-sized patch in the middle of the river, which was lighter and more ruffled than the other, dark green, glassy planes. They had named it the Water Treadmill because here the current flowed at a constant speed and you could swim on the spot. It was the best place, and people were queuing to have a go, but Connie could not do it. Even when she kicked until her muscles burned, the current pulled her backwards to the bank again and again, and all the adults had laughed, apart from Great Aunty Con and Rufus, her Black Russian Terrier. So Connie was sitting with them, in allegiance, holding the wheel of Great Aunty Con's chair.

Aunty Con, and her Welsh accent, and Rufus, and the wheelchair were all part of one novel package and Connie felt splendid being near them.

Today, the aluminium wheels of the electric chair glinted in the sunlight. How captivating they were, with such potential for locomotion!

"Can I have a go on your wheelchair, Aunty Con?" Connie said, reckless after the disappointment of her recent failure.

Aunty Con looked at Connie, that sour look that aggrieved the others and only Connie recognised as a mask, and then a sly smile crept up her sallow cheek, "If you're in here, where will I go?"

"In there!" Connie said, delighted, pointing to the Water Treadmill. Aunty Con's laugh was wet like water running over pebbles and Connie was disturbed. She sat quietly for a moment and stroked Rufus's hot black head. She knew Aunty Con could not walk, but she could swim, Dad had told her, she used to win prizes, but that was before the mountain lake and the disease that got her legs, when her hair was red like Connie's and she wore short dresses. Connie had seen a photograph once, she looked like a different person apart from the same crafty expression. She was still strong though, her upper body was as wide as a shield, and filled the chair, edge to edge. Strong as an ox, she had heard Mum say under her breath to Dad when Aunty Con bent over the side of the wheelchair to swoop Rufus up from the ground and into her lap. Could she really have forgotten how to swim?

When Connie was learning last summer, Mum had said it was like riding a bike, once you'd got it, you never lost it. Connie considered this as she watched a plump pigeon swoop over the river from one tree to another. She remembered the first time she swam, and how her body suddenly understood how floating worked, something clicked into place – like 'unforgetting', and after all those months of splashing and struggling; why didn't they tell you that – the adults? *"You already know how to swim, you just need to remember"* Was it like this for birds too? Did their wings and feathers re-remember the secrets of air and how to move through it?

"You don't need legs to swim just strong arms," Connie whispered to Rufus but it came out louder than she'd planned.

"Connie don't be rude!" the muffled voice came from the direction of the adults and Connie narrowed her eyes at Mum's reddening back. Rufus licked his lips and looked at Connie mournfully.

"He's too hot!" Connie said, bouncing to her feet. She ran to the river's edge and slapped her sides, "Rufus! Come on Rufus!"

"He won't go in unless I do," Aunty Con said. Connie grabbed a plastic cup from the picnic box and filled it with water in the shallows. She returned to Rufus, and poured it gently over his head, "That's better, isn't it Rufus?"

The river rushed under fluttering leaves and the voices of other children rose and fell. Then the breeze dropped and the sounds shifted into a brief stillness and Aunty Con's voice emerged, unfamiliar and expectant.

"If I had the special equipment I could go in..."

"What special equipment?" Connie asked, looking up at Aunty Con whose grey eyes were bright, the plaiting of the river's patina turned in her pupils. She didn't reply.

Dad got up and looked at Aunty Con, then wandered towards the riverbank where he sat on the edge. Connie watched two beads of sweat run down his back, which was as huge as one of the stone boulders she had seen upstream where the rapids leapt. He plopped in and swam towards the Water Treadmill. Connie watched jealously while he moved without moving.

"I'm bored!" Connie said, standing. She walked for a while along the river until she felt lonely.

When she got back the wheelchair was empty.

Barking came from the river, and there they were, Mum and Dad and Uncle Patrick in a struggling, slipping mass, carrying Aunty Con and lowering her in wearing nothing but her big, golden underwear. Connie took her chances and climbed onto the spongy, vinyl seat. She pushed and pulled the lever and the wheelchair travelled smoothly back and forth, the breeze pushed her hair and she inhaled the smell of sweet grasses, so she would always remember, because there, to top it all, was Aunty Con, swimming effortlessly on the spot like a huge golden carp, wide at the top, narrow at the bottom, and Rufus' head like a black anvil, parting the water next to her.

Las Marejadillas*
MARIA JASTRZĘBSKA

There is a place along the river every child knows never to swim in. The water here is so deep, so cold it cuts through your skin and, where the currents meet, a muddy whirlpool sucks everything down as though the river had decided to claim all the debris, broken twigs, pulled roots, scree and any floating animal and carry them to some hoard far below the black surface. There is little light here and so the water which normally shimmers, criss-crossed with sunlight catching in the nets of overhanging branches, is dull, dark with no scattering of light.

But that day the villagers ran to cross the river at any cost. Some still carried knapsacks, suitcases, linen bags filled with whatever they could find that seemed precious. A roll of bedding, a mirror, saucepan, an album of photographs. Others carried their children and it was them they threw first into the water. Some even pushed their neighbours out of the way on the bank, just to get to the river first – anything to flee the footsteps behind them.

You can hear it coming. A low sound not so much like the wind, more surf, sea sucking on stones – sea wolf sucking on barnacle, whalebone. If you shine a torch you can see silver shapes in the distance rear and lobtail over the water. This is where tide meets current. Now the wave appears white-faced on the bend of the river. Foam spurting upwards. Fleet plumes of grey followed by almost see-through whelps. It doesn't yet roar. But its hoarse chuff grows louder until nothing's the same. The river's course has changed and now the water is flowing so fast it brings back everything it once carried out to sea. A red cap, children's shoes, whole trees, tea chests and chains, a boat sliced in half. Everything that drifted gently, now rushes past. The head of what looks like an elk?

*from *The True Story of Cowboy Hat and Ingénue*

Mirror Image
SUE ROBBINS

Under the surface, in negative, hang layers
of folded hills. If your eyes can pierce
the dark you'll detect the shapes of houses,

their gutters, their half-glazed front doors,
sense there must be rooms packed to the gills
with silt, streets filled with lake instead of air

(a shape that won't materialise could be fish...
long hair floating to the surface...).
An effort of concentration lets a certain

shifting of the light linger on the window
of a childhood bedroom, betray the corners
of familiar furniture, tamed by years of water

brushing, rushing past and hollowing out
the shape of things (a pike, mouthing
grainy water to a scattering of small fry...?).

I make no claim to water and its hollows,
or to the shape of things impressed
like watermarks on my mother's dresser.

Unswimming
HOLLY DAWSON

Take a deep breath. Let yourselves go unswimming. No kicks.
No strokes. No holding your breath. You are unborn. Free.
Embrace your natural water state.

I want to push off these tiles and charge into a 100m Freestyle.

Listen: the water is a hum in your ear. Close your eyes, mummas.
Discover your hum. This hum is a gift from the water to you.
Gift this hum to your baby.

I hold my breath and swim underneath them, the water alive
with their mothering hums. I am trapped in a pod of desperate
whales.

Your baby unswims as you unswim. Just float…feel. No swimming
now, mummas.

She's talking to me. I can't talk back. That's the thing with pools.
They rob your voice.

Open your hearts, your wombs, your ears.

She says the three as if they're connected. I hear: tannoy, whistle,
drain. Squealing kids' pool. Roar of the overhead slide.

Feel the water, mummas. Feel your hum.

My water is full of everyone and everything else.

How do you hum disconsolance? How do you hum regret?

————

The unswimmer is my Doula. I'd had problems with Jack. You do with your first. So we're throwing money at our second. We've moved to Sussex. Doulas are part of fitting in.

My Doula says my body is blocked and must be re-opened. Unswimming connects us with our infant selves. She says, *we're taught to swim correctly.* We are told we *need to be safe.* Water becomes *dangerous.* We are labelled *good* or *bad* at the purest, most natural thing in the world. My Doula uses finger quotation marks whenever she's renouncing mainstream culture.

My husband hired the Doula. He was concerned about last time. It took up a lot of his time. He worried we wouldn't have a second. Sven is a diver, not a swimmer. The colder and higher the better. Big splash, big cheer, sprint a few metres then out.

And the women? The women, we swim and we swim and we swim.

———

Although I'm 32 weeks, I covet evening riverbank roll-ups. Sven's away. I have Jack's monitor on. What's this big house for if not secrets?

I clamber through the building site at the end of the garden to the river. My bump scrapes the brickwork. I want to hammer this wall down.

The river seduced us into leaving our London life: canoeists, swans, sunlight. Jack's excitement, and the deep-breathery of it all. The estate agent had the air of revealing a secret. We saw it and signed: a fresh family start.

Then Sven with the builders: glass screen, flint wall, decking. The eyebrow that raised when I suggested a path to the bank to swim. No – the river was beautiful to look at, but unclean, unsafe. He wanted a country pad for City friends to ahhh at. To say: This is what you left London for, with no question mark at the end.

Now Sven's away, the river and I are courting. A toe. Then ankles. Each leg.

Tonight, I untie my hair and lie back in the sweet night grass. My hot neck cools on the silty riverbank mud. I let my head float free in the water, smoke curling up to the sky.

Unswimming, week three. It's also half-term. Sven's away, so I've had to let Jack roam feral around the pool. I float on my back to keep an eye on him, belly high, an island. I imagine my head is a shipwreck, my mind a survivor. My mind swims out for this new land. Will it find redemption there?

But my limbs flail where they used to have skills. Clutching the side, I look for Jack. He's at the top of the slide, looking down at me, watching.

What can he see? Ten blobs bobbing.
He sits without waving like a water-winged god.

What is he thinking?

> This is what a mother is.
> This is what women do.

That evening I go to the river. The wall is higher, the decking almost in. I pick up the builder's mallet and rub it against my cheek. I'm surprised how easily the wall gives when I bash the top bricks in. The moon is full and knowing. I'm sticky from summer days stuck in a body that's not my own. I smoke, undress, slip in.

It's shallow enough to stand in, but deep enough to bob. Trees I haven't learnt yet shadow-rustle overhead. Dark splashes catch my pulse: pikes, rats, leeches, snakes.

I won't let myself get scared. My sister was a wild swimmer. I was always chicken. Rivers are just pools you don't pretend in, she said.

I give myself to the water, rub my belly, hips and thighs. Wide white-thighed woman in this white wide moon. Fat milky fullness makes me floatful and warm. Bump and moon greet each other in sphered recognition.

Night rivers are mirrors to see moons in.

———

Unswimming, week six.

Doula breaks down in changing room. They've said she can't have the pool for another course. Unswimming is a birth-right, she rails. People like this make swimming elitist. *Defy the four-stroke tyranny! Breathe whenever the hell you want!* Unswimming seems less about bonding; more Doula's attempt to radicalise a group of women, fighting for the right of everyone to uterinely bob. The Suffra-wets, if you will.

The day churns on with a mammal-sense I'm due. Fight with Sven on Skype. Nightmare bedtime with Jack.

The river pulls me to it. A surging strength picks up the mallet and demolishes half the river wall. There's something fierce within me that only water can contain. The river says: Do what you will, I'll still go on and on.

Thick silver stillness. I feel you stirring, a deep low flinch. Water must break for us both to be born. I'm not afraid of you, I shout out loud, meaning you, and the water, and myself.

Down the River*
ALEXANDRA HEMINSLEY

The water tasted like nothing I had experienced before. There was no salt, despite us being so close to the sea. It was exactly what I would have imagined this shade of earthy green to taste like. 'Mint and mud', Virginia Woolf called it, and I understood in those moments what she meant. It was silty, but fresh, calling to mind the chlorophyll intensity of spirulina or similarly verdant powders so beloved of health food shops. There was nothing of the familiar chlorine burn in my nose, nor the sting of salt on my lips or eyes. It was fresh.

I smiled to myself, remembering a conversation I'd had with Patrick in the week leading up to the event.

'One of the things you'll notice after all this sea swimming is the cinnamon,' he told me, as I questioned him for the umpteenth time about what it felt like to swim in a river.

'Why is that?' I queried, intrigued by this exotic nugget of information. 'What is in the earth in Sussex that could do that to the taste of water? Or does it just come from the sea?'

'That's just what rivers taste like,' he said with a shrug. 'Especially after the stormy spring we've had.'

I was mystified. It was only when I relayed the entire conversation to D later that evening that he pointed out that Patrick had probably said 'sediment' rather than 'cinnamon'. Ah.

I daydreamed about this former self, the one who had never tasted a river, and after ten minutes or so I looked up, trying to get my bearings. The river was wider than I had expected, much wider than it was in Littlehampton, and the three of us, swimming at a similar pace, were taking wide zigzags rather than staying tight to its curves. I had never seen a river this wide from within. The banks seemed high and inaccessible, whereas we were low, eyes at water level, seeing the world as a duckling might. Like them, I was unable to fly, making our sunken position between the banks an inescapable one. The only way out of the river was to finish the course. There were kayaks within view, but no markers to demonstrate how far we had swum or how far we had to go. And as the route had several curves to it, there was no chance of seeing our final destination yet. I steadied my breath, chose a tree in the distance, and told the others I was aiming for that then planning to take another pause to get my bearings.

And so we continued. Swimming for ten or twelve minutes at a stretch; pausing to right our course, checking that we were all still feeling strong, then onwards. I had swum for an hour continuously in the pool, but it had always been punctuated by pauses in the shallow end. I had at least practiced in open water by now, if only for about fifteen minutes of continuous swimming. But this was unlike anything I had ever experienced: we were inaccessible, plunged into nature, swimming our way home.

A beat started to form as I felt my stroke lengthen and become more confident. My breath, my body, my surroundings. We passed under bridges. We swam alongside curious swans. And I'm sure we passed over more than a few fish. All the while, there was a terrible freedom in not knowing how far I had come and how far I still had to go. Every marathon, every half-marathon, even every 5k training run, had been dictated for so long by pace, time and goals. Now, I had no idea. I knew that I wanted to be swimming, I knew I was swimming, and so I swam. On and on. Exhalation, exhilaration, exhaustion.

This, I suspected, was as close to the state of flow as I had ever felt. I had done long training runs in the past where time had appeared to pass with some elasticity, so complete was my absorption in what I was doing. But this was entirely new sensory territory. With almost nothing to look at beyond my hands' repeated motions and the bubbles they were creating, nothing to hear except the roaring of the water being forced forward by my exhalations, and nothing to taste other than the river itself, my senses seemed to reach a deep state of relaxation.

When I had first moved to Brighton, I'd been transfixed for months by the horizon, finding an enormous sense of rest in seeing the curve of the earth every day after nearly fifteen years in a dense urban environment, increasingly surrounded by screens, walls and endless moving detail. I became convinced my eyeballs were happier – not just my sense of well-being, but my actual eyeballs. When I visited the optician, she confirmed that I was right. When you are always looking at things close to you, the muscles behind your eyes are in a state of almost permanent contraction. By looking into the distance, day after day, those muscles relax; hence the sense that my eyes themselves were happier in their new home. Now, as my eyes had nothing at all to stare at, and my other senses were receiving similarly uncomplicated messages, something inside of me unfurled and let go.

* Extract from *Leap In: A Woman, Some Waves, and the Will to Swim* (Hutchinson, 2017)

Lake, Pool & Pond

Sharrah
LYNNE ROPER

Winter

High on Dartmoor, the Double Dart slows briefly between two sets of rapids to form Sharrah Pool. There are plenty of breathtakingly beautiful places on this stretch of river, but Sharrah is special. It's enchanting, entrancing, and it never fails to throw buckets of Dartmoor pixie-dust at anyone who sees it.

Today there is a sprinkling of snow and it's still falling as we arrive in the glade by the pool. The temperature hasn't gone above freezing for days; it's 3°C in the river. The water is much paler than usual and has lost its deep coppery gleam and black depths. By the rapids, it's almost turquoise, and there's a gelid, greeny tint that I've never seen here before.

Wearing wetsuits, boots, gloves and hats, we slide into the river and swim up the eddy towards the top falls. Ice creeps through the neck of my suit. I dip my face under and taste pure chill; my lips freeze almost immediately. We reach the rapid and throw ourselves off the rock. It's like jumping into a beautiful cocktail made with crème de menthe and the most effervescent volcanic water. The bubbles burst fast on the surface in a shower of sparks like fireworks, and I can hear the fizz above the roar of the waterfall. Then I shoot along as though in the tail of a comet.

Snowflakes drift past. Icicles coat the rocks at the falls, and it's hard to tell them from the gushing spumes of water. The boulders in the glade are iced with snow. Honey jumps between them, following us upstream.

My fingers slowly freeze from the tips down, and after fifteen minutes or so I'm forced to leave this magical water world.

We change, eat shortbread and drink hot chocolate. We dip our fingers in warm water from a flask. Mine are blue and the intense pain whirls me back to my childhood of wet wool socks in wellingtons and winter chilblains.

Spring

We've had several days of positively spring-like weather, and so we set off for Sharrah Pool, warmed intermittently by sunlight through the bare branches. Following the late freeze there isn't so much an unfurling of leaves as a tentative peeking of leaf buds which continue to hug themselves just in case.

The Double Dart is not too full for the time of year and her depths are clear and amber, although there is still a suspiciously chilly-looking greenish-blue tinge around the rapids. We have two temperature takers who say 9°c and 8°c, but it feels colder than that to my stunned body which attempts to shrink inside itself as I slide in. Several of us shriek. Honey cheats by wearing her fur coat.

I swim up and am more or less acclimatised by the upper cascade, where JJ forges across and clings to the far side. The water is gorgeously foaming and sparkling in the sunshine. I go in off an incredibly slippery rock and flail past in the rapid grinning and sinking as the energy fizzes through the needles of icy heat in my skin. I pass everyone else on the way up, faces dancing with light reflected from the choppy surface, hair ruffled by the cheeky gusts of wind funneling down the gorge.

Afterwards we scoff a trio of cakes: gin-soaked lemon drizzle, chocolate, and a colourful dried-fruit fest. I'm grateful for the warmth of my lovely Mammot hoody until Rachel, wrapped in a capacious white robe and carrying a lightsabre, tells me I resemble a sperm.

Summer

The morning deluge is long gone, but the moorland rivers are still rising at tea-time when we meet. Kayaks are spread around the car park, a rare sight in the summer. We peer over the parapet as we cross New Bridge and it scares us. Walking up through mud and dripping trees, we hear the river seethe; it's creamy with foam and the colour of dark chocolate. Parts of the path have fallen away over the summer with the constant rain.

Foam maps the movement of water in Sharrah pool, and there's an eddy I haven't seen before on the far side; the current from the cascade reaches three-quarters of the way down, and the eddy circles in a spiral back up the far bank, like stirred coffee. Usually, there are rock-studded shallows at the lower end of the pool where you drift gently aground before the river is forced in a rapid through the narrows, but today the surge completely covers the rocks and there's a real danger of being swept over. No swimmer would survive that trip. The water is relatively still at the near bank below the entry spot, and we decide we can safely return and exit here. I scan the river for fallen trees, but it looks clear.

We enter the beautiful, chill river and swim with difficulty upstream. It's like being jostled in a mosh-pit; arms and legs are bashed in different directions while our bodies vibrate with the roaring bass notes of the falls. I whack my foot on a rock, having not realised I'd been pushed so far over. We collect foam quiffs and moustaches on the way up to the big boulder where we are able to balance and experience the upper cascade. The energy suffuses me, spray and surging water pulse in time with my blood. I dive forwards and feel like a surfing dolphin in the boiling chocolate water, sinking now and again as I lose my buoyancy.

I return to the top but this time stay longer with the flume and try to enter the circular eddy, but am ripped past. I have to swim flat out to escape to the near bank, my body bending like a banana.

I'm panting with effort and exhilaration. Huge raindrops hit my head, and I float on my back in the eddy while the rain forms little fountains on the surface and the oak overhead bends and rustles its leafy tambourine in the gale.

We barbecue in the rain, talk, and drink wine and beer. A couple of kayakers stop for a chat on their way past. We wander back through the pitch black woods well after nightfall. The foam on the surface of the river glows and illuminates its passage down the dark gorge.

Autumn

I drove across the moors through splatting showers, sunshine and rainbows. Heavy rain overnight had raised the river considerably. Foam billowed on ginger and dun water, and kayakers littered the surface by New Bridge. We walked up the track through squidgy mud and the scent of leaf-mould, once rendered speechless by a glade of zinging yellow leaves still clinging to the trees.

Sharrah appeared through the warm, woodland colours, black water speckled with white flotsam. Today the pool had lost her tranquility, and the surface was in a slow boil. Upstream towards the waterfall the river surged and spray misted the view. I swam towards the falls from the nearly submerged rocks, feet like ice. The cacophony of the cascade intensified and swirled around. The river fought me, forcing me backwards and so I switched from breaststroke to front crawl, puffing from the cold, and with an icy chill reaching my brain through my face. When I made it to the eddy, it was filled with turrets of beery foam like drifts of partially-thawed snow. I reached the central rock, grabbed it and then flung myself into the rapid, shooting downstream among strange little bergs formed from bubbles the size of my head.

As I swam, gold and orange leaves flashed past my hands like autumn fish.

Skye, Diving
KADDY BENYON

Halfway to texting her, I
remember she's no longer there.
Dead a month or more,

I am stalking through heather,
razor grass, tripping up mounds
and over stepping-stones

toward a promise of waterfalls;
deep blue pools. I stop
to snap the imposing purple

spur of a mountain, drop
hurriedly down to a skinny, scree-
littered path to sit and sight it:

her stepped river – emptying
out pocket after pocketful
of glacial waste into hasty water.

I go to it, undress, kneel and assess
the fall. I stand, toes curled over
rock-edge then tip forward,

gently, gently, fly inside spindrifts
and downdrafts of warm, silky
air, float a slow light moment

before breaking the icy skin
of grey-green water
        and buckling

beneath its surface weight,
bubbles of prayer forced from me.
Down there under crag-arches,

an open-mouthed shock billows
around my skin like a Victorian
petticoat. I kick it free, swim

deep enough to run
my palms along the jagged bed
to find just the right river-glyphed

stone: one that retains the snow
it was borne from; cools my cheek
as I write; looks flawless on her grave.

In Deep
CHARLOTTE ANSELL

You are never indifferent;
it is always a case of how and when,
not if.
You want the shock of him,
the affront, the tussle, to succumb,
to be as one, engulfed, submerged.

His skin is dappled,
sun dimpled; the copper ore
of the hills pours down
pooling over pebbles
to kiss his chest,
the rest is shadowed,
cast hunter-green
by the dip and lift of leaves
from trees that hug the bank.

You know better,
he is neither tame, nor kind,
it's not why you came here
but it doesn't hold you back.

You live for summers like this,
to surrender to the dance,
the tingle, the abandon,
surefooted, you offer yourself,
wade in.

Perhaps in a past life
you had scales, a flash of tail.

He is chameleon,
never gives a straight answer.
You see right through him,
it doesn't matter.
You let him have you,
gulp you whole,
you don't say no.

The Mountain's Voice
JENNY ARRAN

Slate smooth.
Amber through darkness.
Tannins of peat and sheep
cropped turf.
Water of rock
and rain
rushed
to stillness.

In this dark pool
under the sky
rock body
holds time
in liquid form.
The mountain's voice.
Its quiet insistence
ripples my listening thoughts

Wrapping its cold question
So neatly around my offering
of warmth
I would dissolve
For its answer.

I swim.
In a dim liminal memory
of time kept silence.
And the quiet grass
and the shining sky.

Water Spirit
CLARE BEST

i

Jack squats
     by the weed-green pool
watching water
        tumble
    swirl and ditch

chasing
    into the drown-dark –
endless flow work

all sap-skin
    Jack sinks
        into writhing wetblack –

head dipping under
       and up

the fierce joy-ache
    of his frozen skull

and the red iron tang

making him
       flip-kick
    spit-laugh
shiver-grin

ii

windhints trick-track
      air teases water
            teases Jack
resting in the deep
inkdark under

      windcricked
Jack slow-turns
lift-drifting
           quicker now
     swells and churns
black stroke blue
    mudspins
         curls
reaches up

bending into sliplight

slick-backed
all awake Jack
    breaks through

and surface-dances

trembling with ripple work

The Non-Swimmer
JILL MUNRO

She learnt to swim in her forties in Berlin, buoyed by sea-salt,
sniffing clean air in the buff, away from chlorine, verruca socks,
pyjamas and clinging costumes – the past pooling of a British
childhood. She'd waited all her life for the urgent lift of water –

to float free like an empty bobbing bottle of India Pale Ale.
Still unsure, she couldn't quite believe her sister's arms
had left her, no longer held her: *You can do it, you can swim!*
She felt that familiar panic, the sinking stomach plunge –

longed for the security of the flailing label – 'Unable to Swim'.
Instead, she swallowed hard, girded and glided with her skill;
river-swimming under waterfalls, rock-lined coastal plunges,
then Sweden's lakes for a water-lillied Valkyrie crossing,

joining nine naked women swimming to their new-found freedom
beneath the wet crackle of a thunderstorm brewing overhead.

In a Blue Lake*
GRAHAM BURCHELL

an expletive came out like a sneeze
when first glimpsed between trees

being three or four times as intense as the sky
a monomictic crater's eye in extinct volcanic maar

no body of water should take colour so far
not even when seventy metres deep

let's consider its small fish lovers of blue perhaps
that evolve to wear it   body   fins   tail   eyes

they'll not be visible to each other of their kind
until autumn starts to wane and the lake dies

to winter grey   a time of recognition
of being in season of falling for
an opposite's cobalt hue

* Blue Lake, Mount Gambier, South Australia

Skinny Dipping at Isola Santa
KATHLEEN JONES

The lake is the blue green of glacial melt-
water, the mountain, upside-down
on its wrinkled skin, rocked by
our naked plunge.
              The fish fry,
little cannibals, nibble my toes
and arms trawl bracelets of weed.
Deeper in, millenniums of dark water
plummet under the blue mayflies darting
electric above its liquid ecology. I feel
the tug of invisible vectors, the chill
of ancient ice.
              Skin to skin,
I am fish, trailing weed, a floating leaf,
a sleek apostrophe curving through
the sun's piercings at the innocent surface.

Lake Ontario
LINDSAY ZIER-VOGEL

The lake is calmer than it was in the morning, but the wind still pushes small waves against the side of the dock, even and steady as a metronome.

Emily dives in, but I take the ladder, rungs slippery with algae. It's cold and now I wish I had jumped in instead. Three-two-one, I tell myself, but still don't push off. Except for staff raining, I haven't been swimming once this summer.

From the sand, the lake looks blue, but at eye-level, it's a thick, dense green. I adjust my goggles. Three-two-and I push off, the cold water prickling along my scalp, filling my ears. I swam fast to shake off the cold, kicking hard – the muted thump of my feet against the surface.

Emily is a strong swimmer and I have to work to keep up. We swim along the blue and white rope, and turn around at the final buoy to head back the other way. I blink through the water leaking into my goggles, Emily's legs glowing to my right and as we swim back and forth and back and forth, I realize how much I've missed this – the rhythmic quiet, tracing a familiar keyhole right, left, right left.

Lake swimming is so much different than swimming in a pool. Here, waves are sporadic and catch you off guard, tripping up your arm, making you misjudge how far you have to turn your head for your next breath. Here, the water gets in your nose so you taste the lake, even if you're careful not to swallow any water.

I wonder how different it would be if this was the ocean – if the waves were governed by tides and undertows instead of winds and boats. I've never swum in an ocean before and wonder if the salt really does make you buoyant.

My ex-boyfriend Matt used to tell me about the sand on the beach near UBC that would stretch forever when the tide was out, then disappear when the tide was in. He got caught on the beach once when the tide came in.

"Why didn't you leave when you saw it coming in?" I asked him.

"It's not like that. It creeps up on you. You know it's coming, but you don't really know until it's there," he had explained. We stopped talking on the phone shortly after that conversation.

I wish I had visited him before we broke up so I could've seen the water pushing right up against the city, the blackberry bushes he said lined the shoreline, the mountains he said turned purple when the sun started setting.

Rescue
SARAH WALLIS

It brings elation, this skinseal
covering of cold, but every swimmer
in wild water deals with fear.

It happened to me in Sweden
under the watchful eyes of an
overprotective father, not mine.

He saw the sink of confidence
as the middle dark drew near,
deep lake water, bottle-green

and hiding maybe-monsters.
Over half way, the ripples
stopped. Each stroke could pull

you under, something unseen
that shivered a signal, and was glad
to drag you down. Everybody on shore,

waved happily, but I was buoyed
to see the father, that wasn't my own,
climb heavily into a rowing boat.

Aquae Sulis
ZEL NORWOOD

I am deep in the curve of her pool
Keeping cupped hands,
Letting warmth cocoon me,
The thermal swirls and mineral souvenirs
Of a ten thousand year journey wash me.
I am drenching myself in millennia
Seeking to cleanse myself of history

And my call to her while present is ancient:
A call for strength,
Abundance and wisdom in mothering,
A call for her help,
Her care, some answer
To a long unanswered wish –
For the remorse of a tormentor,
For release
To move beyond.

I surface on circles –
Rising schools of bubbles –
Feel my weight borne wholly
By her thicker waters,
My face tipped to meet square
Her sharp refractions,
The setting sun slipping strong into the quadrant of vision
Where habit would have me squint, shy,
Shedding tears as she shines.

But braving the strength of the light,
Trusting the circles within the circles –
The gaps of my eyes – to adapt to the rays,
I glimpse my reflection in the lip of glass above –
The pane between me and the sky –
See the shape and power of my shoulders,
The courage worn on my chest,
The abundance of love and age worked, by motherhood,
Into the skin spanning my heart.

And as the bubbles surround me –
Circles within a circle –
I see the face of Sulis
Gazing downwards and upwards,
Looking into the waters of the gap,
Staring into the rounds of my eyes.

Pond Hang
CLARE WHISTLER

Somehow I have got myself
leaning over a branch, legs
hitched wide, on a mossed log
liable to break.

I feel spread, almost
pinned, but happily so,
the branch under my armpits
willow warm, lichen-loved.

And though my feet will
possibly flounder and I am
tipped right forward,
I am again held –

my eyes trembling with pond,
to see how light falls on leaves
through water and how
any shift is a new horizon.

Night Swimmers
ANNA SELBY

Yes the water struck them
brought them back
shrunk them
Yes the water was velvet
Yes the velvet was everywhere
Yes they climbed into a glassy slip
Yes their yeses
reached into each other's yeses
Yes the moon fumbled like a teenager
Yes they both scattered and reformed
Yes the water throbbed
Yes the scent salt and watermelon
Yes they lay in constellations
Yes they trusted the water
Yes eyes shut
Yes green was olive
Yes all their fingertips olive
Yes it stained them
slapped them awake
Yes the water sang with them in it
Yes the echoes of their strokes at the edges
Yes they climb out altered
Yes the lake is the field's birthmark
Yes now her plait is a wet black wire
Yes gloss and molasses
Yes the light on the surface sugared and skitterish
Yes the picture steadies
Yes a drum skin
rattling, remembering them

Lido

They Can't Really Fly
ED BROOM

We took that photo out of its frame, once, but the back was blank. Late 50s, give or take, guessed Nana.

Rationing's over, the sun's out and there they stand, The Flying Squirrels. Working from left to right, there's Terry, confident and every inch a future mayor, stood next to a beaming Frank, already at 30 the pensioner of the gang. Then tragic Jim, blond and scrawny, and finally Rex, swimming cap scrunched into his fist, staring down the camera and giving it the full Charlton Heston.

Isn't hard to see why Nana fell for him. Rex, busy rebelling against everything you've got, is my Grandad.

Posing in front of the gentlemen's cubicles, hands awkwardly clasped around each other's waists, the lads are in the prime of their lives, princes of the pool.

"I ever tell you, Fi, that we could have turned professional?" He'd told me that story a dozen times, maybe more.

"No, Grandad."

"Darn right. Frank's swallow dive was, according to the great Betty Slade, a thing of beauty, the way he hung in the air. Like a Tiger Moth, she said. Terry and Jim we used to call 'the pikies' since they could do a front-back, a back-front, straight or reverse. And my somersault with tuck? Well, ask your Nana." At that point, Nana always rolled her eyes.

"But it wasn't to be, alas. My father insisted, probably quite rightly, that I should learn a trade. Being most at home in the water, I chose plumbing."

Then he'd point at the pine frame on the mantelpiece. "So that's me, Rex Garwood, apprentice plumber, plus three drips." That got a laugh every time.

"And see all those urchins perched on the diving stage? How none of them are on the top board? Don't know how it started, but they had to get the nod from one of us Squirrels. Different times, Fi, different times."

New millennium, new job, Mum had said. Her shifts at the Spar meant that I got offloaded to Nana and Grandad's most weekends. Although he was nearing 60, Grandad walked the half-mile to the pool first thing every morning to fit in his regulation 25 lengths. One overcast Saturday in June, he took me along.

"Don't look so scared, girl. I'm not going to throw you in like I did your mother. I like to think I've learned my lesson."

"You threw Mum in the pool?"

He sighed. "Not my finest hour. She might forgive me one day. Anyway, you OK here? I need to get my yards in."

After ten minutes splashing around in the unheated learners' pool – the original boiler had been requisitioned in the war – I was cold and bored. Wrapping myself in one of Nana's bath towels, I sat on the concrete sun terrace and watched Grandad glide up and down leaving hardly a ripple.

Did I say he swam every morning? Of course, he could only use the lido when it was open, meaning May to September or thereabouts. By Christmas, he'd be carrying a little weight and not quite his summer self. By Easter, he'd be lardy and grumpy. Come June, though, he'd be the man we all loved.

"Grandad," I asked him once, "why don't you go to Splash on the edge of town? They've got a flume, you know."

His eyes had reminded me of that photo. "That's not proper swimming, Fi. I like to feel the rain on my back and the leaves in my hair. Old Frank used to talk about the trees turning copper and gold. We belong here, Rex, he'd say, out in the elements!"

Soon after that, things changed, and not for the better. Nana was diagnosed and Grandad retired to look after her. Thinking it might help, they sold up and bought a tiny flat near the coast.

Nana had to point out that it might be not be too clever for an old codger like Grandad to swim in the sea: "What if you misjudged the tide, Rex?"

Then the council shut the lido. Not sustainable, they said. Grandad joked that it was mostly due to him not going. In truth, he hadn't paid in years, just flashed his cap to the yawning lad on the turnstile.

Around 2010, poor Nana finally succumbed. We feared the worst for Grandad. Sure enough, within a month, he had a stroke, a severe one that knocked out most of his functions. Paralysis. Memory loss. Depression.

"Combination of age and inactivity," said the doctor, "mixed with a large helping of heartbreak."

Mum managed to find a place for him in a newly-built care home not far from ours and, as it happened, within spitting distance of the dead lido, gates still bolted while the council um-ed and ah-ed. I liked to wheel him to the window.

"Look, Grandad. When those branches move, you can see the high board."

Gene Pool Party Dude
MARK FIDDES

If the gene pool had a shallow end
you wouldn't have to swim so quickly
from breast stroke to crawl to freestyle
hoping no one's pissed extra chromosomes
slyly through their happy-go-lucky gussets
while you nosed past limp Elastoplasts
eeling towards the pumps to spawn.

If the gene pool had a diving board
you could pike over your ego's hissing lilo
and the bobbing beachballs of love,
flying through fortune's chlorine reek
to the speed boat where the Playboys rev,
It girls sway and nobody gives a flying fish
which swanky school shrank your soul.

If the gene pool had a chrome ladder,
you could rise lustrous as Burt Lancaster
muscles rilled like sand, tanned as rock
to try all the pools in the neighbourhood,
not submerged in a birthday frogman suit
like Dustin Hoffman, harpoon on guard
against all that's congenitally tentacled.

If the gene pool had been Google mapped,
from a satellite you'd be gobsmacked
you sprang not from an azure rectangle
but a blue guitar, an Elvis bar at the bridge,
fake volcano, wave machine and hula queens,
chuffed your Double Helix was a cocktail
sucked from a pineapple with jokey parasols.

Wake
CLAIRE COLLISON

Whenever he thought of her, it was always
autumn mornings, the water's surface
a sheet of rusting leaves.

Toe edging concrete, he'd toy
with the shock, making pacts:
By the time this train has passed.

The cold seared, shrinking his skin –
his scalp ached with it – but he knew
his own blood would warm him.

Following in her wake, he forgot
and felt everything. She'd find her rhythm
and be lost.

Afterwards, she'd wring out her swimsuit
and drench under hot jets, eyes closed,
feet planted on the wet tiles.

He was left to strip and soap and rinse.
He knew the routine: she'd no time
for boys who showered in clothes.

The Lido Coat
IA JENNINGS

Could you make me a coat
and slip it round my shoulders?
Not a winter coat, not woollen,
sodden with rain,
not waterproof and clammy.
But not a spring coat either.
Emphatically not silk.
Perhaps linen, but not the woven slubby stuff:
more a coat made of the flowers of flax,
the colour of the summer sky, blue
and clear, like water
and equal on a scale with the air,
the water, in an enchanted place.

Too many questions,
too many demands.
For answer, you shove me in the lido:
gasping, I think the cold will kill me,
but the water slips around my shoulders
like a coat, like an embrace,
as I swim my first strokes

Moon
ANNIE PEEL

Head underneath
Where the sound is muted
And the light is refracted

>The fresh tang of chlorine
>Or the pulpy earth

To have the heavy weight of it
Block out the reality above
Spine slicing through the soup of it

>Cradling, warming the blood
>Or punching the breath out

To slither slide through the expanse
With the power to cut a path
By gently parting your hands

>No gravity or joints protesting.
>Your own personal moon.

Take a deep breath and be lifted
Just beneath the surface
To a blurred world
Of stability
Of balance

Out of the echo of the
   Swimming pool chamber
      And under an open sky
         Feeling weightless and limitless

             Until you re-emerge –

                 And the cold air
                 Makes your bones ache

                 And the soft downy hairs
                 on your skin

Are ruffled by a breath passing.

June '16
LOUISA WRIGHT

She bends
around tall mountains, green forests, old tower
blocks and
here, cool water. Long days
of lies and shitty
headlines led to this split. I

watch my arms send the water-shocks
outwards; blue water communion with arc of blue sky.

July, Oxford
JACK PRITCHARD

As I walk to the pool I stretch my arms in front of me,
palms outward, awkward for a moment
then pull back:
a thousand unseen turbulences part, spiral and rejoin.
The afternoon is heavy.

awkward, backward. awkward, backward
upward, I reach, as if I could pull back,
kick off these boots and swim above the terraces, all
dark-moss gutters, and back-garden ponds,
the flash of a glasshouse roof
and further off, the Thames, lacing through pink meadows.

Dive Deep
RACHEL PLAYFORTH

Dive deep
in the pool of tears,
the wood between worlds.
Emerge in another time
where you might belong.
The lido's curves
like an ocean liner
clean blue, wedding white,
the sweep of a staircase
to mirror-clear water.
You try on its riches
its borrowed glamour.
The pool fits and flatters,
a weightless gown,
sunlight like diamonds
laid on green silk.

Laid on green silk
sunlight like diamonds,
a weightless gown.
The pool fits and flatters
its borrowed glamour.
You try on its riches,
the mirror-clear water,
the sweep of a staircase
clean blue, wedding white.
Like an ocean liner
the lido's curves
where you might belong.
Emerge in another time –
the wood between worlds,
in the pool of tears.
Dive deep.

Pickled Sunshine
MICHELLE PORTER

The temperature hits 30 degrees celsius and out they spring, the great unwashed, like whippets from racing traps, hunting for water. Christine is thinking of the Seventies when everything was tinted orange by the everlasting summers – she's thinking of the tangerine and bubblegum-pink wallpaper in her bedroom, of chicken and chips in plastic baskets. She watches her mother in the fresh, blue water, pulling her daughter slowly across the pool on a rubber ring. For all her memories of the slow and scorching summers of that decade, she has no recollection of swimming with her mother. Not at the pool, or the beach, not even at the outdoor lido ten minutes from her childhood home.

Christine snuggles on the grass, eyes shut, the sun burning her back. It is so hot that she doesn't even care about her unshaved bush, the mousy hairs on the inside of her upper thigh. As she drifts into a half-sleep she tries to dredge up possible submerged memories of the London lido, but all she can hear is her mother's voice.

"We're not going to the lido, it's filthy dirty."

"It's too rough."

"You wouldn't like it, it's freezing."

"If you stand on a drugs needle, you could die."

In those years, Christine pestered her relentlessly to go swimming, the long, hot six-week holiday making her bad-tempered with urban boredom.

"I went to the lido once," her mother told her. "When I was in the pool swimming, a pervert stole my underwear. He stood looking over at me grinning, my knickers in his fist." Christine stopped asking after that and over the years the image of the pool grew into a cold, chilling place where plasters and dead leaves floated on the surface of the water. She imagined men in macs loitering behind overgrown bushes.

Sometimes now Christine calculates her daily calories, as if counting sheep to get to sleep. Avocado, 232. Pink French Fancy, 100. Calorie counting – another reason Christine's mother refused to go swimming. She was waiting for her diet to take effect. Once she had lost the baby fat she could buy new clothes, and perhaps then she would think about taking a dip... until that day things were on hold. Whenever she sat on the beach she kept her clothes on as Christine ran into the sea with her dad.

"Be careful!" she'd bellow, as they limped towards the waves over knobbly pebbles.

Christine tried to be patient, but one summer at a caravan park she lost her temper. "Who's looking at you!" she shouted, before casting aside her towel and striding towards the freezing water in her leopard print bikini. Now though she understood it wasn't other people's stares her mother had been worried about: she'd been judging herself. The place where her flat stomach had been: gone doughy and bloated, slashed with the red welts of childbirth. Christine had ruined her mum's figure. So she couldn't go to the lido because it was dirty and rough – and because her mother hated her own body.

Today the pool is full to its brim. Clusters of humanity slather on sunblock thick as paint and huddle, preen and hide under shades. Christine looks down at her own roll of flesh and the size of her thighs, a little closer together this year than the previous summer. She's worked out that if she sits a certain way it disguises the hanging of her bloated gut.

She looks around at the other women and marvels at the variety: some large and tattooed, others with long legs inherited from generations of good middle-class stock, a few so ripe and full at the breast they make her blush. And then comes one of the gazelles, picking her way through the debris of sausage rolls and towels with slender feet, hair cascading to her tiny unstretched waist, skin like polished stone, unblemished. Young. Her eyes follow as the girl makes her way to the back of the pool, to Testosterone Terrace where the teenagers sit and flirt.

She remembers the swimming baths of her teenage years, the changing room wall pierced with holes where the boys would try to catch sight of the girls' naked bodies as they changed. The girls would fill them in with balls of toilet paper to protect their modesty and the boys would poke them out again. She scans the water for Ruby, who is flapping her hands in joy as her grandmother bursts up from under the water. She wants to pickle this moment in sunshine and keep it forever.

Tired from the sun and water, they have all stopped talking for a while. Ruby stands shivering in her towel, waiting for her grandmother to unpack their knickers from inside her waterproof coat. Christine squeezes her mother's shoulder affectionately and smiles. She won't tell Ruby about the strange man in the lido, and together the three of them will create new memories. Of hot summers cooled by the thrill of cold water. And Nanny, diving into the deep-end having forgotten to remove her glasses.

The Swancote
LYN THOMAS

I was a land-locked child, living on the boundary of town and countryside in the Midlands, in the middle of everything, neither one thing, nor the other.

Brooks and streams were the only water within reach, and they were almost always the destination of my childhood wanderings. One stream became a ford, crossing the road; on fine days I paddled in it with my friends, sunlight through overhanging trees illuminating our joyous faces.

The brook was much nearer our house and a more regular haunt. It was dark and murky, and we were in terror of falling in, but fascinated by the flora and fauna that lived in or near it. We picked the wild flowers that grew on its banks, looked longingly at the yellow flags that grew just out of our reach, brought tadpoles home in jam jars. The tadpoles did not last long, despite or perhaps because, of my constant attentions. I compensated for their early demise by conducting elaborate funerals, and placing one of my mother's best vases on their grave.

Really hot weather was a rarity, and if the heatwave came on a Sunday something extraordinary might happen. I would be playing in the garden, laboriously filling my old baby bath with water and sitting in it, naked apart from sunglasses. Suddenly my Dad would say, "Let's pack up and go to the Swancote". Sandwiches would be made, bottles of squash and a thermos of tea. And off we would go in the Ford Prefect, driving in to unknown territory on the other side of the town. In the back of the car I would be feeling sick, but determined not to delay our journey to a place I associated with the deepest form of bliss. Then arrival, through the turnpike gate, the first sight of the pool, the fountains, the towels and picnic bags and people. We would find a place on the scarcely visible grass, then Dad and I would change and get into the water. I would bob about in my yellow and white plastic swimming ring, while Dad kept a sharp eye on me. Mom couldn't swim, but she sometimes donned a costume and stood in the shallow end, just to cool off.

Sometimes my cousin Peter and his Mom and Dad came with us. Then Dad had to keep an even sharper eye on us children, because Peter was very ill, and likely to bruise or bleed at the slightest touch. There is a photograph of the three of us in the fountain at the Swancote. It was probably one of the happiest days of Peter's short life. He is smiling, the fragility of his small sickness-battered body exposed in a ruched costume. I am brown and blonde, glowing with health and the joy of living. My father's gaze is intense, protecting Peter from the sharp edges of the world, from the invisible harms that in the end would take him from us. But for now, at the Swancote, he is with us, enjoying the cool water, the sensation of the grass underneath his feet, the warm air.

Later we will eat the cheese sandwiches, appetites sharpened by the fresh air and the swimming. Then home, where I run around the garden singing at the top of my voice, full of delight to discover that there are places in the world that seem specially designed for my pleasure. I was still land-locked but I had the cool blue depths of the Swancote in my soul.

Pool Closed Today
MARTIN GAYFORD

The pool closed today for
half an hour during the
lightning. Everyone was
asked to leave with the
loudspeaker, and we were
left listening to the women
talking about how their
folding chairs go together.
It should be safe to go in.
The lady that joined us is
sitting on the bench, she
can't get up from this
spot very easily.

The folding chairs are
still there and we're moving
them in with the table tennis
table this week. Our teacher
encouraged us to take
something from here and
there and put them together
on the canvas. That night
we saw *Rebecca*. It was
scary. 'We're going to get
struck by the lightning, right
now! Everybody look out
for the lightning!'. Girls,
stop shrieking. 'She's my
sister though!'.

Contributors

Charlotte Ansell has been published by Flipped Eye with a third collection forthcoming in 2017. Publications include *Poetry Review, Mslexia, Now Then* and *Butcher's Dog*, and anthologies including *The Very Best of 52* and *WordLife*. She won the Red Shed Poetry Competition in 2015 and the Watermarks Poetry Competition in 2016.

Jenny Arran is a visual artist. She grew up in North Wales, loving the wildness, rivers, rocks and the sea. Her poems and paintings reflect a sensory and relational connection to nature. She swims regularly in Pells Pool, as well as the river and sea near Lewes, and takes her children, on holidays, to the pool in her poem.
jennyarran.co.uk

Redfern Barton has lived in many countries but now lives in Sussex. She mainly writes about the natural world and our relationship with it. Her non-fiction work *A Gentle Year,* based on a blog and a lifetime of jottings in notebooks, is due for publication in 2017. A recent poem, *'Evening Song,'* was set to music by the composer Josh Urben and performed locally in 2016. She is a photographer and collector of unconsidered trifles, an almost daily beach wanderer who nowadays prefers to swim in warmer waters.
summerstarfield.wordpress.com

Kaddy Benyon's first collection, *Milk Fever,* won the Crashaw Prize, and was published by Salt in 2012. She is a Granta New Poet and former poet-in-residence at The Polar Museum in Cambridge, where she wrote poems in response to Hans Christian Andersen's *The Snow Queen* as part of a collaborative 'text and textiles' exhibition with costume designer Lindsey Holmes. Kaddy is a member of the Newnham Riverbank Club in Cambridge where she wild swims with her daughter.

Clare Best's first full collection, *Excisions,* was shortlisted for the Seamus Heaney Centre Prize 2012. Other poetry publications include *Treasure*

Ground, Breastless and *CELL*. Clare's prose memoir was a finalist in the Mslexia Memoir Competition 2015. *Springlines,* a collaborative publication with the painter Mary Anne Aytoun-Ellis – and part of their project exploring hidden and mysterious bodies of water – will be pulished by Little Toller in 2017. Clare is a university teacher of creative writing and a co-founder of *Needlewriters,* the quarterly reading series in Lewes, Sussex. She has been a keen swimmer all her life.
clarebest.co.uk

Emma Beynon, brought up on a farm in Rhossili, spent every summer as a child swimming between coves and hurling herself into the wild westerly waves, only coming out of the sea for a can of Coke and some crisps. When it became clear, as a bit of a dreamer, Emma would not become a farmer, she started to write, teach and sail a Bristol Channel Pilot Cutter in the Arctic. Emma now lives in Mid-Wales, swims in the River Wye and teaches creative writing for Arts Alive Wales to young people in search of adventure.

Mark Bridge usually writes for other people, so it's a novelty for him to see his own name in print. He's spent the past fifteen years as a self-employed copywriter, crafting sentences for assorted high-street retailers and big brands, from technology companies to tourist attractions. Mark currently lives in an East Sussex village, where he awaits the arrival of medical nanobots to upgrade him. Only then will he swim like an eel.
markbridge.info

Ed Broom works in IT but tells his children that he's a lighthouse keeper. He lives in Ipswich on Broomhill Road, at the top of which sits Broomhill Pool, a Grade II listed lido built in 1938.

Graham Burchell was born in Canterbury and now lives in South Devon. In between he has lived in Zambia, Saudi Arabia, Tenerife, Mexico, France, Chile and the United States. He has an MA in Creative Writing from Bath Spa University and has published four collections of poetry. He was the 2012

Canterbury Festival Poet of the Year, a 2013 Hawthornden Fellow, winner of the 2015 Stanza competition and runner up in the 2016 BBC Proms Poetry Competition.
gburchell.com

Claire Collison – writer, visual artist – swims whenever and wherever she can and is a member of Tooting and Brockwell Lidos. She teaches creative writing and runs workshops inspired by place. Claire was artist-in-residence at Brockwell Lido, and is currently artist-in-residence at the Women's Art Library. Her first novel, *Treading Water*, was a finalist in the Dundee Book Prize. She has been shortlisted for the Bridport Prize and the Flambard Prize, and came second in the Resurgence Prize. Her poetry is published in *Templar Anthology*, *Butcher's Dog*, *South Bank*, *Yorkshire Mix*, *Island Review* and *The Compass*.
writingbloomsbury.wordpress.com

Holly Dawson is a writer and editor based in rural Sussex. She grew up swimming and surfing the wild seas of the north Cornish coast, then Cape Town's two oceans and the gentler rivers of France. She is a regular swimmer at Pells Pool, her local lido in Lewes, where this story was born, and runs Lewes Short Story Club.
hollyjdawson.com

Mark Fiddes is the author of *The Rainbow Factory,* launched last September, and *The Chelsea Flower Show Massacre* (both Templar Poetry). A graduate of Merton College, Oxford, he spent a number of years in Washington, D.C. as journalist before working as a creative director in Soho, London. Recently he's been runner-up in the Bridport Prize and winner of the Dromineer Festival Prize, among more than a dozen other awards, and has been published in *The London Magazine*, *The Irish Times* and *Southword Journal*. His favourite swim is across the Colomers lakes in the Spanish Pyrenees.
markfiddes.wordpress.com

Martin Gayford was born in London in 1971. He lives in Lewes, East Sussex and has been an advocate of and frequent visitor to Pells Pool for 15 years. Martin's 2015 collection *I Forgot To Tell You, I Really Enjoyed That Sandwich*, published by Spiralbound / Susakpress, features several poems written poolside, and others inspired by time spent there. **martingayford.wixsite.com/gayfordmartin**

Malinda Green is an author and award-winning writer who is inspired by close encounters of the natural kind. These include swimming with a seal last summer in a secret cove in South Devon, where she lives for part of the year. Mal is currently researching and writing a novel that combines the edge of knowledge neuroscience with old wisdoms on a search for missing jigsaw pieces.
thedailymalblog.wordpress.com

Tara Gould is a writer who feels very fortunate to live in Lewes, where she has discovered a wild swimming hot spot of rich and diverse variety. When weather permits, she enjoys nothing better than slipping down the muddy banks into the river Ouse at Barcombe Mills, or ducking beneath the salty swell at Seaford, or soaking up sun on the grassy plains of Pells Pool after two dozen *long* lengths, (dripping wet, dreaming up tales). More of her short stories can be found on her website.
loneranging.wordpress.com

Tom Hall is an English writer and a Londoner. He lives there in order to swim year-round at Highgate Men's Pond and take his family to Parliament Hill Lido on sunny days. He has written on travel for many newspapers and magazines and works at Lonely Planet, the travel guide people, as Editorial Director.
@tomhalltravel

Alexandra Heminsley is the author of *Running Like a Girl,* which has now been published in fifteen countries. She is a journalist, broadcaster and ghostwriter. She lives in Hove.
@hemmo

Maria Jastrzębska's most recent collection was *At The Library of Memories* (Waterloo Press 2013). Her selected poems, *The Cedars of Walpole Park*, have been translated into Polish by Anna Błasiak, Paweł Gawroński and Wioletta Grzegorzewska (Stowarzyszenie ywych Poetów 2015). *Dementia Diaries*, her literary drama, toured nationally with Lewes Live Lit in 2011. She was co-editor of *Queer in Brighton* (New Writing South 2014). Her translations of Justyna Bargielska's selected poems *The Great Plan B* are forthcoming from Smokestack Press in 2017. Treading water in pyjamas won her a school lifesaving bronze award. She has loved water all her life.
mariajastrzebska.wordpress.com

Kathleen Jones is a poet and biographer living in an old mill beside the River Eden in the Lake District. Summer evenings are quite likely to finish in the water, watched by the resident heron. She has just returned from swimming on a coral reef in Cambodia. Kathleen has a pamphlet, *Mapping Emily*, forthcoming from Templar Poetry this year and a full collection, *The Rainmaker's Wife*, from Indigo Dreams.
kathleenjones.co.uk

Seema Kapila is a singer/songwriter, poet and short story writer with previous work published by The Frogmore Press. Her stories weave tales about people she has known, places, communities and time. She lives in a creative corner of East Sussex with her husband, two children and their cat. She has an immense respect for nature, camps as often as she can, and is fascinated by the healing power of natural running water.

Anna Kisby grew accustomed to cold water and big waves as a child, in the Atlantic off Cape Cod. As an adult, she spent 20 years swimming in the Channel off Brighton (with a brief interlude in London where she was a fan of Brockwell Lido). She won the Proms Poetry Competition 2016 and was commended in the Faber New Poets Scheme 2015-16. Now Devon-based, she swims mostly in the River Dart.

Ia Jennings used to swim at Brockwell Lido in South East London. With the tall trees in the park surrounding the lido, it never felt like swimming in a city. Lolling around on the decking with friends, in for another dip, sunbathing, chatting, moving around to catch the sun's last rays as evening came on, then jumping in for that last swim of the day... Ia moved out of London in 2015 to be by the sea, and near another lido – Saltdean, re-opening in 2017. In the meantime, Pells Pool has cast its spell, with its deliciously fresh water and lovely setting.

Hannah Linden has been published in several magazines, was commended in the 2015 Prole Laureate competition and won the Cheltenham Compound Competition 2015 for collaborative poetry with Gram Joel Davies. She loves wild swimming in lidos (Brixham's Shoalstone Pool is a regular), the sea and especially in rivers. This poem was inspired by swimming in her favourite spot on the River Dart at Stillpool (a five-minute walk from where she lives). She loves wild swimming because it stills her mind. This poem is about the particular quality of swimming in water rich in peat.

Mary Lowerson has been fascinated by water from early childhood. Living inland, opportunities for total immersion were limited to the local outdoor baths in St Albans. Since then Mary has swum in rivers, lakes and the sea around the British Isles, hot springs in New Zealand and the fjords of Norway. The sea also inspires her work as an artist.
mclowerson.wixsite.com/mary

Tim Martindale is a writer-ranger. He holds a doctorate in anthropology from Goldsmiths and is a graduate of The Creative Writing Programme, Brighton. He has researched and written about Cornish fishing communities and is currently working on a book about belonging and wayfinding. Although he enjoys wild, mountain swims when he can, like Carver he best loves coastal rivers, and so finds himself, incurably, forever drawn back to Cornwall.
timmartindalewriting.com

Jill Munro has been widely published in various poetry magazines. She has been long-listed three times for the National Poetry Competition and her first collection *Man from La Paz* was published in 2015 by Green Bottle Press, London. She won the Fair Acre Press Pamphlet Competition 2015 with *The Quilted Multiverse*, published April 2016 by Fair Acre.
www.poetrypf.co.uk/jillmunropage.shtml

Zel Norwood is a psychologist and poet whose writing often explores patterns in nature and myth and their resonances with human adaptation and growth. Zel lives in a Sussex village but grew up near Bath in Somerset, which she continues to visit regularly. Whenever possible, she takes to the city's natural thermal waters associated with Sulis, the local Celtic goddess of 'the Waters of the Gap'.

Jeremy Page grew up on the Kent coast in sight of France and has swum in the Channel every summer for more than half a century. He now lives in Lewes and teaches at the University of Sussex. He is the author of four pamphlets and two full collections of poetry, most recently *Closing Time* (2014) and *Stepping Back: Resubmission for the Ordinary Level Examination in Psychogeography* (2016). He has also published translations of Catullus, Leopardi, Rimbaud and Boris Vian. His plays *Loving Psyche* and *Verrall of the White Hart* were performed in Bremen (2010) and Lewes (2014) respectively.

Annie J Peel is a poet and playwright living in London. She has sampled many of the lidos and outdoor swimming places that London has to offer, with the Hampstead Ponds remaining a firm favourite. But none quite compare to the river in a village in Herefordshire where she grew up. Many a happy summer afternoon was spent there.

Jane Greene Pettersson is a swimmer, teacher and writer. She teaches people of all ages and abilities to swim, specialising in those who have a fear of water. Jane swims outdoors whenever possible: in the summertime this is in the rivers and lakes of Sweden and Finland and in the Baltic sea. Jane has written poems, short stories, and articles on swimming and diving, and has co-written three books on coaching that have been translated into several languages. She writes a blog about swimming.
mindfulswimming.org

Rachel Playforth is a poet, librarian and editorial board member of the Frogmore Press. She has been a regular swimmer at Pells Pool for over twenty years.

Michelle Porter was born and raised in south-east London when the Post Office tower was still the tallest building in the sky. Her earliest memory of swimming is falling into a lake in Suffolk where she encountered a man in an antique helmet; even at 5, she was good at telling stories. Michelle now works as a content writer, writing fiction, non-fiction and everything in between. In 2017 she was awarded the Creative Futures Gold Prize for Prose at London's Southbank Centre. She now lives in Lewes, East Sussex where she regularly takes a chilly dip in Pells Pool.
portersbespoke.wordpress.com

Jack Pritchard takes any opportunity to take his clothes off and plunge into cold water. His favourite place is Long Bridges in Oxford, an old river pool on the edge of the Thames. He spends his time watching bees, and meandering along the footpaths and waterways of southern England. He has been described as a 'wandering poet'.

Emma Pusill (Plum Duff to her swimming friends) turned to outdoor swimming, aged 40, to conquer fear: fear of fish, of failing, of ageing. She's winning with the fish and ageing. Most at home in the sea, she also has a powerful love for lidos. She is co-writing *The Lido Guide* and blogging about her lido road trips. In 2016 she was involved with organising the inaugural National Lido Conference, and work has begun on the 2017 event. She is a trustee of Portishead Open Air Pool.
unbound.com/books/lidoguide medium.com/@lidoguide

Sue Robbins is a member of a group of poets local to Lewes who meet regularly to share their writing. She has spent many summers sitting on the grass at Pells Pool watching her children in their element, and remains somewhat in awe of anyone who can feel so comfortable in the water.

Lynne Roper developed a love of water during her Devon childhood, and it never left her. After early careers in the RAF and academia, she became a paramedic. Turning to outdoor water after a double mastectomy, Lynne wrote powerfully – in her blog and for the Outdoor Swimming Society – about the risks, joys and deep friendships that came with wild swimming. She died of a brain tumour in August 2016, aged 55. A book of her collected writings, *Wild Woman Swimming,* is planned for 2018.

Rebecca Rouillard was fortunate enough to grow up in Durban with a pool in the back garden and spent all her summer waking hours in the water—not only swimming but also playing games, reading books and eating meals. She currently works as a freelance writer and designer, lives just outside London with her husband and two children and swims at various places including Shepperton Lake, Tooting Lido, Hampton Pool and Dorney Lake.
ninepmwriter.co.uk

Anna Selby is a naturalist, poet and dance collaborator. She writes mainly about water, and has run poetry and wild swimming workshops for Wilderness Festival and The Poetry School. She leaps into all waters all year round, swimming regularly at Hampstead Heath ponds in London. Pushkin used to break the ice with his fist and Rupert Brooke would sneak out at night to dive into the black Cam as it rushed by his house: to jump into cold, wild water is an act of rebellion, an affirmation – we do it so as not to be tamed.

Janet Sutherland has three poetry collections from Shearsman Books, of which *Bone Monkey* (April 2014) is the most recent. She is currently working on her fourth collection with Shearsman, due out in 2018. Her work has appeared in many magazines including *Poetry Review*, *New Statesman*, *New Humanist* and *The North* and her poems are widely anthologised: from *The Virago Book of Love Poetry* to *The New British Poetry 1968-88* (Paladin). She is a founder member of the *Needlewriters* cooperative, which organises poetry events in Lewes. She lives in Lewes very close to Pells Pool. **janetsutherland.co.uk**

Patrick Taggart was born in India and grew up in Ireland and England. He was spurred into trying to find some form of creative expression in 2014 by his (now grown up) children, Ben and Emma, who are both talented in visual arts. A pen seemed more manageable than a paintbrush, so he decided to give poetry a go. Patrick lives in Northern Ireland and enjoys swimming off its coast and in its lakes and rivers.
letgoandjumpin.webeden.co.uk

Rosamund Taylor learnt to swim in Sandycove Harbour, Co. Dublin, and has always drawn inspiration from the sea. Her poems have twice been shortlisted for the Montreal International Poetry Prize. In 2016, Rosamund gave a reading at the Cork International Poetry Festival, and was published in *Magma, Agenda, The Penny Dreadful*, and *Banshee,* among others. Her poem, '*The Minotaur's Mother*', won the Readers' Award for *Orbis,* Issue 175.

Wayne Tenyson kicks around Lewes. This poem is a memory
of swimming at La Plage De Roi in the mountains above Uzes
one September.

Lyn Thomas has published a memoir, *Clothes Pegs: A Woman's Life
in 30 Outfits* at clothespegs.net. In a series of short texts, the memoir
captures the stages and moments of class transition, emerging sexuality
and white femininity through depictions of the lived experience and
social contexts of wearing and buying clothes. Lyn is the author of two
books and several articles and chapters on contemporary French writer
Annie Ernaux. She has also published on feminist fan cultures, *The
Archers*, lifestyle television, religion and media, and on working-class
whiteness. She is currently part-time Professor of Cultural Studies at
Sussex University.
clothespegs.net

Mat Christian Thomas is a writer and photographer. He swims
in rivers.

Louisa Thomsen Brits is an author, outdoor swimmer, littoralist and
mother of four. Louisa is interested in the overlooked details of ordinary
lives and liminal places. She writes about the nature of things, our
interconnectedness and the rhythms and rituals that unite and define us all.
@L_Thomsen_Brits

Sarah Wallis is a poet and playwright living in Leeds, West Yorkshire.
She often works with magical realism, always with an element of playful
observation, and has been published in numerous journals. She has a
poem in the forthcoming Yorkshire Poetry Anthology, '*The Bellymen of
Wakefield Town*', and her pamphlet, *Waterlore*, was highly commended in
the recent Mslexia Pamphlet Competition. Sarah's nearest lido is at Ilkley,
on the edge of Ilkley Moor, a freshwater, unheated pool with outstanding
views that holds an annual summer solstice swim.

Clare Whistler is an artist working in performance, site specific work, poetry, music, visual art and landscape. Drawing upon movement and gesture, she responds, interprets and collaborates with people, places and the elemental. Water has been the source of her work for the last five years with projects *Stream*, *UnderwaterEdge* and the annual *WaterWeek*: 7 days of information, conversation and reflections celebrating water both local and global, created with Charlotte Still. She has swum for the last six years in the swimming pool in Stykkishólmur, Iceland.
clarewhistler.co.uk
underwateredge.wordpress.com

Louisa Wright is an editor who lives, works and swims in Lewes.

Lindsay Zier-Vogel is a Toronto-based writer, arts educator, swimmer and love letterer. Her work has been published in various publications including *Where The Nights are Twice as Long* (Goose Lane Editions, 2015), *The Lampeter Review*, *Taddle Creek*, *room of one's own*, *Grain* and *Descant*. She is a creator of and contributor to the popular swimming blog, *Swimming Holes We Have Known*, and has featured on CBC Radio's Metro Morning. Her handbound books of poetry are in the permanent collection at the Thomas Fisher Rare Books Library. Lindsay is the creator of *The Love Lettering Project*, an internationally-acclaimed art project that has been bringing anonymous love letters to strangers since 2004. She is currently working on a Love Lettering Project book and a novel, titled *The Opposite of Drowning*, set next to a lake.

Acknowledgements

For vision, skill and support: Alexandra Loske, Managing Editor of
The Frogmore Press; Rob Read, Commissioning Editor for Pells Pool;
Neil Gower, cover design; Rebecca Souster, publishing consultant at
Clays; Lulah Ellender, proof-reader and copy-editor; Mathew Clayton of
Unbound for masterclass in book production; and Raphael Whittle for
book design and typesetting.

Extract from *Leap In* (Hutchinson: 2017) courtesy of the author, Alexandra
Heminsley © Onion Publications Ltd

For permitting extracts from the writing of Lynne Roper, heartfelt thanks
to her family: Mike, Jenny, David and Ian.